ENERGY SCIENCE, ENGINEERING AND TECHNOLOGY

U.S. ENERGY INDUSTRY RESPONSE TO SEVERE WEATHER

HARDENING AND RESILIENCY EFFORTS

ENERGY SCIENCE, ENGINEERING AND TECHNOLOGY

Additional books in this series can be found on Nova's website under the Series tab.

Additional E-books in this series can be found on Nova's website under the E-book tab.

ENERGY SCIENCE, ENGINEERING AND TECHNOLOGY

U.S. ENERGY INDUSTRY RESPONSE TO SEVERE WEATHER

HARDENING AND RESILIENCY EFFORTS

ILYA BERTOLUCCI
EDITOR

New York

For permission to use material from this book please contact us:
Telephone 631-231-7269; Fax 631-231-8175
Web Site: http://www.novapublishers.com

Additional color graphics may be available in the e-book version of this book.

Library of Congress Cataloging-in-Publication Data

ISBN: 978-1-62808-944-8

Published by Nova Science Publishers, Inc. † New York

CONTENTS

PREFACE

This book focuses on the measures that refiners, petroleum product pipeline operators, and electric utilities in the Gulf Coast have taken to harden their assets and make energy supply to the Southeast more resilient. Discussions with the public utility commissions identified additional sources of information on storm hardening in extensive dockets, and focused on the segments of the energy industry that contribute most to the delivery of gasoline and diesel to the Southeast, United States.

Chapter 1 - In an effort to better understand what actions the energy industry has taken in response to the 2005 and 2008 hurricane seasons, the U.S. Department of Energy, Office of Electricity Delivery and Energy Reliability (DOE/OE) conducted research to identify specific industry efforts related to storm hardening and resiliency. The resulting study focuses on the measures that refiners, petroleum product pipeline operators, and electric utilities in the Gulf Coast have taken to harden their assets and make energy supply to the Southeast more resilient.

Chapter 2 - Hurricanes Gustav and Ike struck the U.S. Gulf within two weeks of each other in September 2008, severely damaging energy infrastructure and disrupting oil and gas supplies throughout the United States. Millions of electricity customers lost power as the storms knocked down thousands of miles of transmission and distribution lines, and forced shut hundreds of substations. Two nuclear power plants were shut due to the storm. Extended electricity outages delayed the restoration of refineries, pipelines, gas processors, and other energy facilities that depend on grid-delivered power.

Oil and gas platform operators shuttered offshore production in the Gulf of Mexico as a precaution before both storms and damage caused by the storms kept a significant portion of that production offline several months after the storms passed. Some smaller platforms were completely destroyed and a small amount of Gulf of Mexico oil and gas production is likely to be permanently lost. Hurricanes Gustav and Ike also shut onshore natural gas processing plants and several gas pipelines, restricting the flow of gas throughout the United States for weeks. Despite the supply curtailment, natural gas prices remained stable both before and after the storms made landfall.

U.S. petroleum supply was also impacted by the hurricanes, which shut key petroleum infrastructure, including refineries, ports, waterways, and pipelines. More than a dozen refineries were shut as a precaution before each hurricane, but only a few remained offline for several weeks after Hurricane Ike due to lack of power supply. Port closures disrupted crude oil and petroleum product imports into the Gulf and once ports reopened, product imports were limited by stringent quality standards for gasoline and distillate fuel. Although stocks of petroleum products were sufficient in the Gulf, the closure of key product pipelines, ports, and waterways prevented many of these supplies from reaching consumer markets. Fuel supply problems were particularly acute in the Southeast, which is highly dependent on supply from two key petroleum products pipelines fed by Gulf refineries. A combination of supply shortages and panic buying occurred in the Southeast in the weeks following Gustav and Ike. Spot gasoline and diesel prices briefly spiked as Hurricane Ike approached and the market anticipated serious damage to Texas refineries but quickly returned to pre-storm levels after site assessments revealed only minor damage.

Chapter 3 - Statement of Patricia Hoffman, Assistant Secretary, Office of Electricity Delivery and Energy Reliability, U.S. Department of Energy.

In: U.S. Energy Industry Response ...
Editor: Ilya Bertolucci

ISBN: 978-1-62808-944-8

Chapter 1

HARDENING AND RESILIENCY: U.S. ENERGY INDUSTRY RESPONSE TO RECENT HURRICANE SEASONS*

Mindi Farber-DeAnda, Matthew Cleaver, Carleen Lewandowski and Kateri Young

EXECUTIVE SUMMARY

In an effort to better understand what actions the energy industry has taken in response to the 2005 and 2008 hurricane seasons, the U.S. Department of Energy, Office of Electricity Delivery and Energy Reliability (DOE/OE) conducted research to identify specific industry efforts related to storm hardening and resiliency. The resulting study focuses on the measures that refiners, petroleum product pipeline operators, and electric utilities in the Gulf Coast have taken to harden their assets and make energy supply to the Southeast more resilient. A summary of the findings of energy industry hardening and resiliency activities is provided in Table ES-1.

* This is an edited, reformatted and augmented version of the Office of Electricity Delivery and Energy Reliability, dated August 2010.

The effort is based on public information from Internet research and interviews with a small number of refiners, petroleum product pipelines operators, and electric utilities. Discussions with the public utility commissions identified additional sources of information on storm hardening in extensive dockets. OE also coordinated with the DOE Office of Fossil Energy and Policy Office, the Energy Information Administration, the Government Accounting Office, the U.S. Department of Transportation Pipeline and Hazardous Materials Safety Administration (PHMSA), and the Department of Homeland Security's Transportation Security Administration. A total of 14 energy companies were interviewed from February through April 2010. The information gathered during the discussions is proprietary. Due to the Paperwork Reduction Act, OE was limited in the number of companies it could contact within each of the energy sub-sectors.

The study is focused on the segments of the energy industry that contribute most to the delivery of gasoline and diesel to the Southeast U.S. Therefore, the focus is on hardening and resiliency efforts undertaken by refiners, pipeline operators, and electric utilities with transmission and distribution (T&D) assets. It does not address hardening and resiliency efforts undertaken to support power generation, Gulf of Mexico offshore production, natural gas processing, industrial gas production, port operations, rail movements of ethanol and propane, or waterborne movements via tankers and barges.

Hardening refers to physically changing the infrastructure to make it less susceptible to damage from extreme wind, flooding, or flying debris. Hardening improves the durability and stability of energy infrastructure, making it better able to withstand the impacts of hurricanes and weather events without sustaining major damage. **Resiliency**, by contrast, refers to the ability of an energy facility to recover quickly from damage to any of its components or to any of the external systems on which it depends. Resiliency measures do not prevent damage; rather they enable energy systems to continue operating despite damage and/or promote a rapid return to normal operations when damages/outages do occur.

A summary of hardening and resiliency actions reported by petroleum and electricity companies in the Gulf Coast and Southeast regions is included in this report. It is intended to educate and inform, not to advocate a particular policy. Energy companies will continue to make investments and pursue technological solutions for years to come in order to maintain energy sector hardening and resiliency.

Table ES-1. Summary Findings of Energy Hardening and Resiliency Activities

		Industry Activities	Refineries/ Pipelines	Electric T&D
Hardening	Flood Protection	Building/strengthening berms, levees, and floodwalls	√	
		Elevating substations/control rooms/pump stations	√	√
		Relocating/constructing new lines and facilities	√	√
	Wind Protection	Securing cooling towers	√	
		Improving tank integrity	√	
		Protecting cabling	√	
		Protecting retail outlets	√	
		Upgrading damaged poles and structures		√
		Strengthening poles with guy wires		√
		Burying power lines underground		√
	Modernization	Upgrading electrical systems	√	
		Installing/utilizing cogeneration	√	
		Enhancing IT and telecommunications	√	
		Deploying sensors and control technology		√
		Installing asset databases/tools	√	√
Resiliency	General Readiness	Conducting hurricane preparedness planning and training	√	√
		Complying with inspection protocols	√	√
		Managing vegetation		√
		Participating in mutual assistance groups		√
		Improving employee communications and tracking	√	
		Installing redundant communications	√	
		Procuring mobile command vehicles	√	
		Purchasing/leasing portable generators	√	
		Pre-positioning and pre-wiring portable generators	√	
		Securing alternate sources of gas supplies	√	
		Purchasing or leasing mobile transformers and substations		√
		Procuring spare T&D equipment		√
	Storm-Specific Readiness	Maintaining minimum tank volumes	√	
		Wrapping/protecting pumps and motors	√	
		Facilitating employee evacuation and reentry	√	√
		Coordinating priority restoration and waivers	√	
		Securing emergency fuel contracts		√
		Supplying logistics to staging areas		√

Petroleum Infrastructure Hardening

Flood damage is the most common and costliest type of storm damage to petroleum infrastructure, and results in the longest disruption durations for refineries, pipelines, and terminals. Refiners and pipeline operators harden their assets through flood protection, wind protection and modernization.

Flood Protection

Common flood protection structures such as floodwalls, levees, and berms may be built by either government or industry. The U.S. Army Corps of Engineers (USACE) built a15-foot-high concrete floodwall that protects the BP, Marathon, and Valero refineries near Texas City, Texas. USACE also built the Mississippi River levee system, which provides flood protection to 15 feet for refineries located near New Orleans. Refiners built the floodwalls along the Houston Ship Channel and around Pascagoula to contain a 100-year storm surge. One refiner reported that it has erected a 12-foot high, one-half-mile-long floodwall in 2004 for approximately $4 million.

Elevating substations, control rooms, and pump stations above the likely flood level is another common hardening practice. In many cases, facilities were elevated 15 - 25 feet above ground. Costs for elevating facilities vary depending on the size of the unit, how much power is carried, and how much wind and storm surge that the unit is designed to withstand. According to one refiner, costs may range from $500-900 per square foot, based on the various attributes of the facility and the project design.

Wind Protection

Although hurricane-force winds are not as destructive to petroleum infrastructure as flooding, they still can cause severe damage to refineries, pipeline tank farms, and retail outlets. Refinery cooling towers are especially prone to wind damage. High winds can cause the fan blades inside a cooling tower to become dislodged and launched from the tower if they are not secured. This renders the cooling tower unusable and creates airborne debris that can cause further damage. During Hurricane Rita in 2005, fifty percent of the cooling towers at Port Arthur refineries were damaged and fifty-four percent were damaged at Port Neches, according to a National Institute of Standards and Technology reconnaissance report.[1] Several of the refiners reported that they have installed special braces to stop the fan blades from dislodging.

Tank operators reported that an inexpensive way to harden storage tanks is to install wind girders. In addition to deflecting wind, girders can reinforce the structural integrity of the tank, preventing a collapse.

Modernization

To compensate for aging petroleum infrastructure, companies are updating electrical systems and technology in their control rooms. Several companies have also enhanced their IT and telecommunications infrastructure in preparation for storms to ensure that communications remain operational. For example, after Hurricane Katrina, Valero set up 20 satellite phones and about 40 cellular and radio phones to communicate between its Louisiana and Texas refineries.[2]

Petroleum Infrastructure Resiliency

Petroleum companies follow best practices and undertake resiliency measures as general precautions, or they may take them in preparation for specific storm events.

General Readiness

General readiness activities reported by companies include preparing and updating hurricane preparation plans and purchasing or leasing large-size portable generators. Preparing a hurricane preparation plan and conducting training were reported as general resiliency activities by all companies interviewed.

All companies reported purchasing or leasing portable generators to provide electricity to critical facilities during outages. Economic considerations determine whether refiners and pipeline operators choose to purchase or lease generators. A typical 2-MW trailer-mounted unit costs approximately $1 million or more with accessories and financing.[3] To avoid a recurrence of the shutdowns it experienced during the 2005 hurricane season, Colonial Pipeline purchased 12 trailer-mounted Mitsubishi portable generators, seven transformers, and miles of associated cabling in 2006.[4]

Companies reported pre-wiring and pre-positioning smaller generators at key service stations along evacuation routes. Even undamaged service stations require emergency power to reopen. All petroleum companies that operate retail stores in the Gulf and Southeast indicated that they have pre-wired at least some of their stations. In fact, Florida has enacted legislation requiring gas stations within a half mile of evacuation routes be equipped with a back-up electrical generator. In addition, all owners of more than ten gas stations in a county must (within 24 hours) have a generator installed at ten percent of their fuel outlets.[5]

All of the refinery and pipeline operators for the study indicated that the safety of their employees is paramount. Petroleum companies have numerous methods of keeping track of their employees and communicating with them before, during, and after a hurricane. These methods include websites, hotlines, and media channels, and are aimed at ensuring employee safety and enabling a quick and coordinated response after a storm has passed.

Storm-Specific Readiness

A common storm-specific resiliency practice reported by companies is maintaining minimum product volumes in storage tanks. Above ground storage tanks are at particular risk during storm surge flooding since they can actually float off their foundations when spill-containment areas become flooded with water. Ensuring that an adequate amount of product is in the tank prior to a storm adds weight and stability to the tank and prevents it from floating off its platform.

Electricity Infrastructure Hardening

Electricity is a critical element of the highly interdependent energy supply and distribution system. A refinery or pipeline pumping station, even if undamaged by a hurricane, will not be able to operate without access to electricity. Most utilities have active plans in place to harden their infrastructure against wind and flood damage. In fact, since 2005, multiple State public utility commissions have issued rulemakings and/or regulatory activities related to electricity infrastructure hardening. Many of the T&D hardening and resiliency initiatives taken on by utilities have been in response to such regulation.

Wind Protection

Hurricane-force winds are the primary cause of damage to electric utility T&D infrastructure. All of the utilities interviewed for this study have identified upgrading poles and structures with stronger materials as a primary hardening strategy. For distribution systems, this usually involves upgrading wooden poles to concrete, steel, or a composite material, and installing guys and other structural supports. Although transmission system outages do occur, about 90 percent of all outages occur along distribution systems.[6] Transmission structures are typically upgraded from aluminum to galvanized steel lattice or concrete.

Placing utility lines underground eliminates the susceptibility to wind damage and lightning that is typically experienced with overhead lines. However, underground utility lines present significant challenges, including additional repair time and much higher installation and repair costs. Company interviews indicate that burying overhead wires costs between $500,000 and $2 million per mile, plus expenses for coolants and pumping stations. Perhaps the most important issue for coastal regions is that underground wires are more susceptible to damage from storm surge flooding than overhead wires.

Flood Protection

Common hardening activities reported by utilities to protect against flood damage include elevating substations and relocating facilities to areas less subject to flooding. Unlike petroleum facilities, distributed utility T&D assets are not usually protected by berms or levees. Utilities reported that it is far less expensive to replace a T&D facility than to build and maintain flood protection.

Utilities report that a number of substations along the Gulf have been elevated as much as 25 feet based on predictions for a category 3 storm. Elevating substations to category 4 or 5 storm surge levels was not common since the costs are significantly higher and storms of that magnitude are relatively rare. Utilities have opted instead to invest in spare equipment to address that risk.

Other common hardening activities include relocating critical facilities away from flood prone areas, strengthening existing buildings that contain vulnerable equipment, and moving equipment to upper floors where it will not be damaged in the event of a flood.

Modernization

The electricity T&D system is aging, and to counter the effects of aging infrastructure, utilities are supplementing hardening practices with the implementation of new technology such as improved supervisory control and data acquisition systems, GIS systems, and advanced switching mechanisms to self-diagnose and repair problems and promote greater efficiency of the grid. As Hurricane Ike approached the Texas coast in 2008, one utility used GIS-based damage prediction models to approximate how many customers would lose power, what the infrastructure damage would be, and how quickly repairs could be made. After the storm, they used GIS to create maps of damaged areas and share the information with customers, media, government, and support agencies.[7]

Electricity Infrastructure Resiliency

Common resiliency practices reported by utilities for general readiness include pole maintenance, vegetation management, use of mobile transformers and substations, and participation in mutual assistance groups.

General Readiness

Pole inspection and maintenance is the most common resiliency activity reported by utilities. It is performed both year round and in preparation for particular storms. Pole inspections maximize T&D asset life, gather the information necessary to manage and prioritize asset needs and resources, and minimize unscheduled or emergency maintenance. Southeast and Gulf Coast utilities have instituted a multi-year inspection and maintenance cycle for all transmission circuits, a multi-year wood pole treatment cycle, and a galvanized steel painting program to prevent corrosion on steel structures.

Another common resiliency practice reported by utilities is vegetation management or clearing potentially damaging tree limbs and other vegetation from power line rights-of-way. Although tree-related damage is more common on distribution lines, tree related transmission outages are also a regular event. In 2006, the North American Electric Reliability Corporation introduced the Transmission Vegetation Management Program.

Utilities reported using mobile transformers and substations to temporarily replace damaged assets. A mobile substation includes a trailer, switchgear, breakers, emergency power supply, and a transformer with enhanced cooling capability. These units enable the temporary restoration of grid service while circumventing damaged substation equipment, allowing time to repair grid components. Mobile transformers are capable of restoring substation operations in some cases within 12-24 hours.

Companies routinely update their hurricane preparedness plans and train staff throughout the year. Many utilities reported participating in regional mutual assistance groups in which member utilities voluntarily share staff and equipment in a coordinated response to electrical outages.

Storm-Specific Readiness

A common storm specific readiness activity reported by companies is to secure fuel contracts for post storm recovery needs such as emergency operations and repair vehicles. Most of the companies reported having fuel contracts in place to cover fuel for emergency vehicles and small portable generators, which are necessary to power operations and IT sites. At least one company reported that its emergency plans arrange for skid tanks – portable fuel tanks used for refueling vehicles – to be delivered to pre-determined locations following a storm.

General Resiliency

Both petroleum and electricity companies reported that a primary storm preparation activity is to secure exemptions from evacuation orders in advance so that restoration efforts can begin as soon as possible after a storm strikes. Companies work with Federal, State and local governments to procure exemptions. It was also reported that in some cases, a small number of employees will shelter in place at storm-hardened facilities during a hurricane to monitor the facilities and identify areas that need repair.

BACKGROUND

U.S. petroleum supplies are often impacted by hurricanes, especially major Atlantic hurricanes making landfall along the Gulf Coast States of Alabama, Mississippi, Louisiana, and Texas (see Figure 1). Most notably, in 2005 and again in 2008, major hurricanes[8] hit back-to-back, severely damaging energy infrastructure and disrupting oil supplies throughout the United States. Fuel supply vulnerabilities in such emergencies can be particularly acute in Florida, which is supplied by ports, and in the other southeast States, such as Georgia, South Carolina, North Carolina, and Tennessee, which receive their supply from two petroleum product pipelines fed by Gulf Coast refineries.

Within the U.S. Department of Energy (DOE), the Office of Electricity Delivery and Energy Reliability (OE) is the lead office responding to energy emergencies. OE produces *Situation Reports* that have been the source of official DOE information on impacts to energy infrastructure from events of national significance since 2003. As part of its mission, OE tracks the dates of energy infrastructure shutdowns and restorations. Compiling essential data from the individual *Situation Reports*, OE compared the impacts of the 2005 and 2008 hurricanes on energy infrastructure, based on the breadth and duration of the various shutdowns.[9]

The Southeast is particularly vulnerable to retail and wholesale gasoline price run-ups and supply shortages because of their limited supply options after major storms such as hurricanes. Independent marketers in Georgia, Tennessee, and the Carolinas were hit particularly hard in September 2008 when their regular supply sources were put on allocation (i.e., were only receiving a certain percent of their planned deliveries of fuel), and the independent marketers did not have contractual arrangements with major suppliers at alternate terminals. Shortages caused by refinery shutdowns due to electricity outages and other causes resulted in reduced supplies into the Colonial Pipeline system, which runs from Houston, Texas, to Linden, New Jersey. Panic buying by consumers may have also contributed to shortages at gas stations in Atlanta, Charlotte, and Nashville in September 2008. Prices of $4.00 or more per gallon were reported throughout the Southeast in the days immediately following Hurricane Ike.

Congress held hearings to inquire about the reasons for these shortages, and to encourage the development of solutions. In response to these hearings, OE continued to investigate the root causes of the Southeast petroleum shortages. The OE investigation found a number of contributing factors:

- The Southeast (defined for this report as Florida, Georgia, North and South Carolina, and Tennessee) is served by a minimal number of inland terminals, which are fed primarily via pipeline from Gulf Coast refineries. There is only one major refinery in the region, and (excluding Florida and western Tennessee) limited port and river systems to sustain waterborne movements of products.

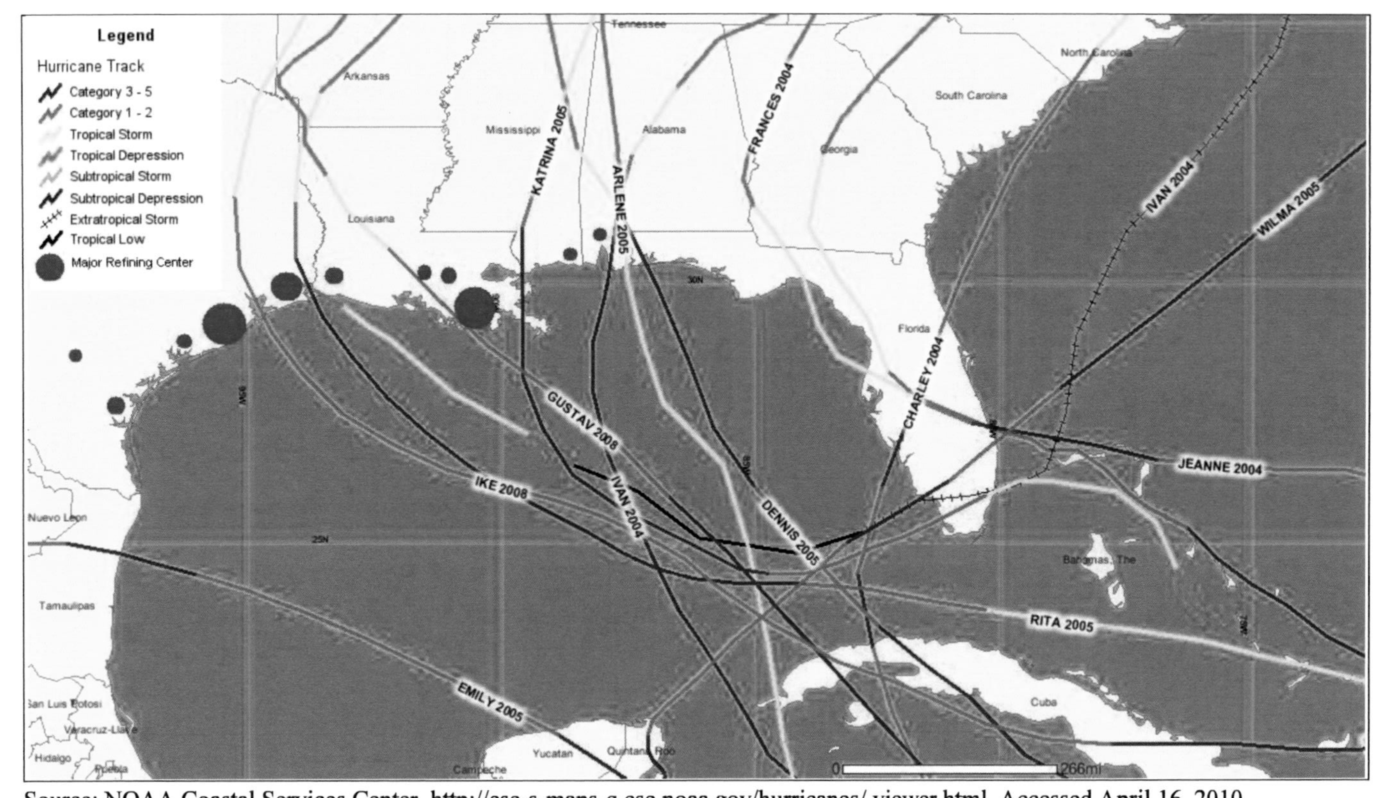

Source: NOAA Coastal Services Center. http://csc-s-maps-q.csc.noaa.gov/hurricanes/ viewer.html. Accessed April 16, 2010.

Figure 1. Refining Centers in Path of Major Atlantic Hurricanes 2004-2008.

- Many Southeast markets depend on petroleum product pipelines as their only source for delivery of gasoline and diesel; some of these markets are not served by a main line, only a pipeline spur.
- Up to one week prior to the anticipated landfall of a hurricane, refinery production and port receipt of imports are reduced or shut down. When a hurricane hits, refineries and terminal operators must also have their storage tanks filled to a certain level as a precaution against tank movement from storm surge or flooding, a measure that prevents them from moving a significant amount of existing stored product into the marketplace.
- Pipeline systems slow their deliveries and impose allocation[10] on customers when supplies are limited. When terminals are on allocation, only those petroleum wholesalers under contract with them may receive product.
- Gasoline is not a homogenous product nationwide. In the summer, some States and counties require the use of gasoline with low volatility (as measured by Reid Vapor Pressure, RVP).[11]

  In the Gulf and Southeast, only select counties in Texas are required to use reformulated gasoline (RFG) year-round. As a result, refiners and terminal operators cannot always assist each other with supplies without special waivers from the U.S. Environmental Protection Agency and/or State agencies.
- Hurricanes often hit in mid-September when gasoline supplies are turning over from summer grades to winter grades. At this time of year, refinery, pipeline and terminal operators begin to reduce their lower volatility grades and begin building up winter-grade stocks. This transition may complicate the ability to maintain a steady supply of gasoline during a fall storm event.
- Extended refinery shutdowns lasting two to three weeks are caused primarily by a lack of electricity supply rather than onsite damage.[12]
- Loss of electricity to pump stations can cripple pipeline movements of petroleum products. Pipeline operators require hundreds of staffers and contractors to deploy emergency generators, transformers, and all the associated cabling necessary to keep supplies moving.
- Natural gas and industrial gases are needed to operate boilers and processing units at refineries. If these gases are not available when a refinery is ready to restart, restoration is further delayed.

The above factors can combine to cause product shortages in the Southeast that can persist beyond the immediate storm emergency, potentially disrupting product availability for as long as several months.

In the fall of 2009 OE began identifying industry efforts to storm-harden energy infrastructure and expedite restoration from storm-related outages. During this initial phase of the inquiry, it quickly became apparent that many refiners, pipeline operators, and utilities had already invested significantly in hardening and resiliency measures. In response to this finding, OE expanded the scope of its inquiry, and began a second, more in-depth study of the specific measures taken by owners and operators of energy infrastructure. This report is the result of that effort.

FOCUS OF THE STUDY

Identifying which segments of the energy industry contribute most to gasoline and diesel disruptions in the Southeast United States was paramount in order to focus on only those relevant segments highlighted in Figure 2. An extremely wide range of assets supports the production and delivery of petroleum products to the Southeast, but not every asset is significant in terms of its contribution.

The simplified energy flow diagram in Figure 2 illustrates the interdependencies between petroleum, natural gas, industrial gases (e.g., hydrogen, nitrogen, and oxygen), and electricity. Crude oil extracted from the Gulf of Mexico or imported by very large tankers is the feedstock for Gulf Coast refineries. The majority of the platforms in the Gulf of Mexico are small- capacity, unmanned facilities, and the loss of a dozen of these platforms would not stop the flow of crude oil to the Gulf Coast refineries. The current approach by platform operators is to fully shut down and evacuate all manned facilities when a hurricane or tropical storm enters the Gulf of Mexico. Likewise, tankers laden with crude oil imports will also wait out a storm. Fortunately, substantial crude oil stocks on land and potential access to the Strategic Petroleum Reserve guarantee several weeks of continued crude supplies to refiners.

Offshore natural gas from Gulf of Mexico platforms is directed via pipeline to natural gas processing plants and then on to power plants, refineries, petrochemical plants, and other industrial facilities in the Gulf Coast. Refineries cannot operate without natural gas, as it is critical for boilers and other processing units. Coastal refiners look for alternate inland sources of natural gas during emergencies, e.g., when Gulf of Mexico production is too low to keep pipelines flowing.

Refineries also depend on industrial gases, catalysts, and other specialty products, particularly when restarting following a shutdown. Many refineries are located with or near industrial gas plants to guarantee their supply of hydrogen, nitrogen, and oxygen.

When refineries are unable to operate, refiners try to maintain supply outflow by using product stocks, exchange agreements, and product imports. For example, while Florida's Atlantic ports receive regular petroleum product imports; the rest of the Southeast has limited access to tankers full of imported gasoline and other products, relying instead on pipeline movements of products from Gulf Coast refineries.

Some refineries cogenerate their own electricity, but the bulk of electricity required by refineries comes from the electric utility transmission system. Depending on the size of the facility and the configuration of the grid, refineries receive electricity through either the transmission or distribution network. There is substantial excess power generation capacity in the United States, and the shutdown of a few large power plants will not generally result in the loss of power to refineries, as long as the transmission or distribution lines leading to those refineries remain intact.

Most of the refineries serving the region are in the Gulf Coast states of Texas, Louisiana, Mississippi, and Alabama. Refineries are located on rivers, inter-coastal waterways, or directly on the coast to facilitate receipt of tankers at ports and provide access to the substantial cooling water required for their processes.

If a refinery is unable to operate due to damage or a lack of crude oil, natural gas, or industrial gas, products can still be moved from storage into pipelines and barges as long as the refinery has electricity. In 2005, for example, damaged refineries with operable pipeline/dock/terminal networks received imported products by tanker at their docks and moved those products into the Colonial and Kinder Morgan Plantation pipelines. Petroleum pipelines require a constant flow of products into the system in order to deliver volumes at terminals. Pump stations positioned strategically along the pipeline boost the movement of the product and require electricity to operate. Product pipelines are the primary way gasoline and diesel are supplied to the southeast States of Georgia, North Carolina, South Carolina, and Tennessee.

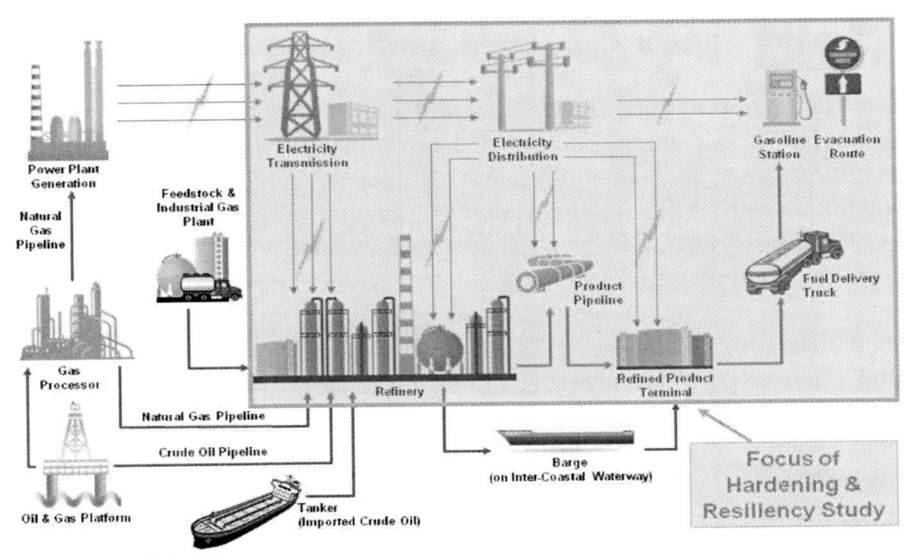

Source: SAIC, 2010.

Figure 2. Focus of Hardening and Resiliency Study.

Terminals provide storage tanks and interconnection with transportation modes (pipeline, barge or small tanker, railroad, and truck) at strategic locations near demand markets. They are privately owned, often by third parties who are neither refiners nor pipeline operators. Companies moving product along pipelines arrange for sale of their volumes to wholesalers and jobbers who deliver the product to retail outlets. Electricity from distribution lines is required to operate the terminals and the pumps and valves that control the flow of fuel.

The delivery of fuel to first responders and gasoline to fueling stations along evacuation routes is an essential step in preparing for an emergency. Maintaining the flow of gasoline and diesel during restoration and recovery from the emergency is also of critical importance. Electricity is also needed to operate the fuel pumps and to track the purchases at retail outlets.

Following this logic, OE determined the most critical energy infrastructure needed to deliver gasoline and diesel to the Southeast (see the blue box in Figure 2, above). The study then focused on the measures that refiners, petroleum product pipeline operators, and electric utilities in the Gulf Coast have taken to harden their assets and make energy supply to the Southeast more resilient.

Aging Infrastructure and Hurricane Hazards

The Nation's energy-delivery infrastructure is composed of an intricate web of electricity transmission and distribution systems, pipelines, refining facilities, and terminals that has grown increasingly complex and interdependent. This infrastructure is aging. Most of the electricity transmission system, which stretches nearly 200,000 miles, was designed to last 40 to 50 years.

In some parts of the country however, it is now 100 years old.[13] About half of the Nation's 2.4 million miles of oil and gas pipelines were built in the 1950s and 1960s.[14] The newest greenfield oil refinery in the United States was built in 1976.[15] The first refinery in the Gulf Coast was built in 1897 and others quickly followed.[16] One of the greatest challenges facing the industry is retrofitting this existing infrastructure with modern technology to improve the efficiency and resiliency.

Aging infrastructure is more susceptible than newer assets to the hurricane-related hazards of storm surge, flooding, and extreme winds. Overall, storm surge and flooding cause more devastation than wind, both in terms of energy infrastructure and human life.

Storm Surge and Flood Damage

A storm surge is a large dome of water, 50 to 100 miles wide, that sweeps across the coastline near where a hurricane makes landfall. Its height is the difference between the observed level of the sea surface and the level that would have occurred in the absence of the hurricane. Storm surge does not exist as long as a hurricane is out over the open ocean; it is a phenomenon that is strictly associated with hurricane landfall.

Since 1900, flooding caused by storm surge has killed more people in the United States than all other hurricane-related threats combined, including freshwater flooding, winds, and tornadoes.[17] Although the number of yearly fatalities from hurricane storm surge has been drastically reduced over the past 30 years, it is still the greatest potential threat to life and property associated with hurricanes. Salt water is particularly destructive to energy infrastructure because it corrodes metal, electrical components and wiring. Certain building components cannot withstand any exposure to water. Plaster, wallboard, insulation, and electronic components are examples of materials that must remain permanently dry. Wood components may also be susceptible to damage from trapped moisture. Flat roofs, common in the Southeast, are particularly susceptible to leaking after high wind stress.[18]

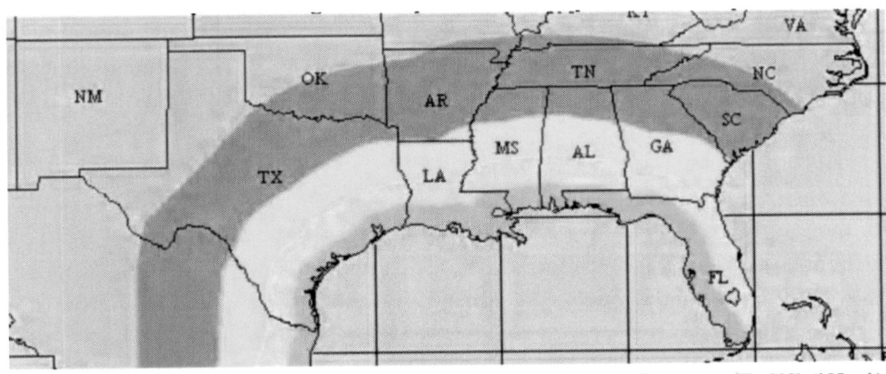

Note: The rotating wind speed of a hurricane is distinct from the forward speed, which can vary significantly. The colors indicate the rotating wind speed of the storm as it travels inland.

Source: http://www.nhc.noaa.gov/HAW2/english/wind/gulf_121.shtml, accessed June 5, 2010.

Figure 3. Extent of Inland Winds from Category 3 Hurricanes 121 mph Rotating Wind Speed and 20 mph Forward Speed.

The National Oceanic and Atmospheric Administration (NOAA) and its National Hurricane Center (NHC) and Weather Forecast Office do not have a specific storm surge scale. These agencies maintain that such a tool would not be accurate or effective at conveying the storm surge threat because of the many variables affecting storm surge, which include:

- Size of the hurricane
- Lack of correlation between rotating wind speed and the height of the storm surge[19]
- Forward speed of the hurricane
- Angle of storm attack to the shoreline
- Coastal topography
- Local bathymetry (slope of the Continental shelf). The shallow Gulf waters off of Texas enhance storm surge, for instance, while the significant ocean depths off of southeastern Florida inhibit surge.[20]

Wind Damage

Hurricane-force winds have the power to transform ordinary objects and debris into high- velocity projectiles. The ensuing damage can take on a domino effect, bringing down trees, transmission towers, distribution poles, and cooling towers. Even underground utility lines can be taken out by uprooted trees. The result of this type of damage can be long-term power disruptions.

Because hurricanes rotate in a counterclockwise direction, the strongest winds in a Gulf Coast hurricane usually occur on the right side of the eyewall[21] of the storm. Because of these increased winds, the right eyewall of a hurricane is also the location of the greatest storm surge. Wind speeds decrease significantly once the storm is over land and cut off from the sustaining heat and moisture provided by ocean or Gulf waters. The strength of the storm and the speed with which it moves over water determine how far inland its winds will reach (see Figure 3).

Approximately 50 miles inland from where Hurricane Gustav made landfall as a Category 2 storm, electrical poles were broken off, transformers were hanging upside down from broken poles, electrical wires were lying on the roadways, and long lines of utility poles were leaning towards the west. The majority of utility poles in the area were no longer upright.[22] Gustav was a slow-moving storm with a forward speed of 10 mph after making landfall. Hurricane Katrina made landfall as a Category 3 storm with a forward speed of 22 mph, so its inland winds reached further than Gustav's and resulted in more damage.

Definitions

In addition to identifying types of infrastructure and types of storm damage, this investigation also had to determine precise definitions of hardening and resiliency. Much of the existing literature on the topic confuses the two terms.[23] This study seeks to differentiate the two terms in order to identify the measures that industry has undertaken under each.

Hardening involves physically changing infrastructure to make it less susceptible to damage from extreme wind, flooding, or flying debris. Hardening measures include adopting new technology, installing new equipment, constructing protective barriers, or changing communications/IT at the facility. Hardening usually requires significant investment by the energy company. Some projects take years to complete; for example, large earth-moving equipment may be brought in to build a new dike or levee. Sometimes the sheer magnitude of assets involved (e.g., thousands of wooden distribution poles) requires years of concerted effort to upgrade.

Hardening improves the durability and stability of energy infrastructure, making it better able to withstand the impacts of weather events without sustaining major damage. Actions taken by industry to harden its assets include:

- **Flood Protection**
  - Building/strengthening berms, levees, and floodwalls
  - Elevating substations/control rooms/pump stations
  - Relocating/ constructing new lines and facilities
- **Wind Protection**
  - Securing cooling towers
  - Improving tank integrity
  - Protecting cabling
  - Protecting retail outlets
  - Upgrading damaged poles and structures
  - Strengthening poles with guying
  - Burying power lines underground
- **Modernization**
  - Deploying technology
  - Upgrading electrical systems (e.g., with battery backup & uninterruptible power supplies)
  - Installing/utilizing cogeneration
  - Installing asset databases/tools
  - Enhancing IT and telecommunications (e.g., adding Internet Protocols, phone lines, video- conferencing)

Resiliency, by contrast, refers to the ability of an energy facility to recover quickly from damage to any of its components or to any of the external systems on which it depends. Resiliency measures do not prevent damage; rather they enable energy systems to continue operating despite damage and/or promote a rapid return to normal operations when damage/outages do occur. Hurricane resiliency activities can take the form of general readiness practices, or measures taken in preparation for a specific storm. General readiness measures are those that apply well to any storm situation, and may be considered best practices. Storm-specific measures are those that may be practical or cost-effective only when implemented for a particular event. Resiliency measures under these two categories include:

- **General Readiness**
  - Conducting hurricane preparedness planning and training
  - Complying with inspection protocols
  - Managing vegetation
  - Participating in mutual assistance groups
  - Improving employee communications and tracking
  - Installing redundant communications
  - Procuring mobile command vehicles
  - Purchasing/leasing portable generators
  - Pre-positioning and pre-wiring portable generators
  - Securing alternate sources of gas supplies
  - Purchasing or leasing mobile transformers and substations
  - Procuring spare equipment
- **Storm-Specific Readiness**
  - Maintaining minimum tank volumes
  - Wrapping/protecting pumps & motors
  - Securing exemption from evacuation orders
  - Coordinating priority restoration and waivers
  - Securing fuel contracts for emergency vehicles
  - Expanding deployment staging areas

Study Methodology

OE began its investigation with Internet searches, gathering information on key topics – electricity transmission, electricity distribution, refineries, petroleum product pipelines and terminals, flood protection, wind damage, and relevant codes and standards.

Researchers identified facility operators that would be appropriate for potential interviews, based on the facilities' relative importance to Southeast gasoline and electricity delivery. Due to the Paperwork Reduction Act, OE was limited in the number of companies it could contact within each of the energy sub-sectors. Discussions with the public utility commissions in Louisiana and Texas confirmed the interview selections and identified additional sources of information on storm hardening in extensive dockets and PUC-initiated surveys, studies, and university research.

OE coordinated with the DOE's Office of Fossil Energy, Policy Office, Energy Information Administration, the Government Accounting Office, and U.S. Department of Transportation Pipeline and Hazardous Materials Safety Administration (PHMSA) and the Department of Homeland Security's Transportation Security Administration. Initial calls included State agencies in Louisiana and Texas. OE's telephone interviews maintained sensitivity to the fact that energy companies are subject to multiple government requests for similar information.

The interview questions addressed:

- Physical changes (new equipment and/or retrofits) to harden facilities
- Best practices to improve resiliency
- Changes made to IT and communications to improve reliability
- Most cost-effective improvements

A total of 14 energy companies were interviewed from February through April 2010. The information gathered during the discussions is proprietary. This report draws on the discussions, but does not reveal the source of any information unless an alternate open source is available. Specific hardening and resiliency plans, activities, budgets, and costs are footnoted.

Limitations of the Study

The purpose of this study is to gain an understanding of the hardening and resiliency efforts undertaken by industry after the 2005 and 2008 hurricane seasons. It is prepared to educate and inform staff at DOE and other agencies. It is not intended to advocate a particular policy or address specific actions or recommendations to industry owners and operators. Its focus is on hardening and resiliency efforts undertaken by refiners, pipeline operators, and electric utilities with transmission and distribution (T&D) assets. It does not address hardening and resiliency efforts undertaken to support power generation, Gulf of Mexico offshore production, natural gas processing, industrial gas production, port operations, rail movements of ethanol and propane, or waterborne movements of fuels via tankers or barges.

To minimize duplication of efforts by other government agencies and reduce burden on industry, OE sought open-source information first, and complemented that with telephone interviews and email exchanges. No confidential information is revealed in this report. The report does not attempt to quantify the benefits of hardening and resiliency. Where available, dates and costs on specific measures are provided.

PETROLEUM INFRASTRUCTURE

Refineries are integrated facilities containing processing units, storage tanks or terminals, feeder pipelines, ports, control rooms, and IT/communications. Some have electricity cogeneration units on site. They are operated by thousands of employees and contractors. A dozen refiners operate 33 refineries along the Gulf Coast (see Figure 4). These refineries have the capacity to process 7.2 million barrels per day, representing 41 percent of the installed U.S. refinery capacity in 2009.[24] Significant numbers of Gulf Coast refineries were shut down in both 2005 and 2008:[25]

- On the worst day in 2005 (September 25, 2005), 20 refineries with a capacity of 4.9 million barrels per day were shut down in the Gulf
- On the worst day in 2008 (September 14, 2008), 15 refineries with a capacity of 3.9 million barrels per day were shut down in the Gulf

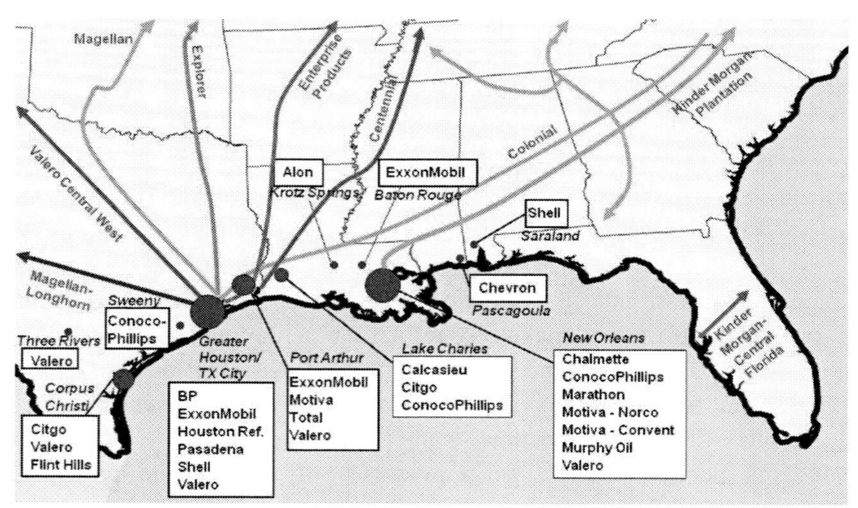

Source: SAIC, 2010.

Figure 4. Major Refineries and Product Pipelines in the Gulf Coast Region.

During the hurricanes of 2005 and 2008, petroleum refineries along the Gulf Coast were subject to flooding and wind damage that caused product shut-ins. Refinery restarts were delayed by extended power outages, as electric utilities struggled to work around their damaged T&D grid, and the supply of crude oil, natural gas, and industrial gases necessary to resume production were slow to arrive.

Pipelines provide another major link in the supply chain of petroleum products. A large number of petroleum product pipelines in the United States originate in either Louisiana or Texas (see Figure 4). Recent mergers in the industry have further reduced the diversity among pipeline operators. Two pipelines – the Colonial and the Kinder Morgan Plantation – deliver petroleum products to the Southeast States. Parts of Tennessee are also served by the Centennial pipeline. These pipelines share common terminals with other pipelines, and as a result, impacts from reduced rates and/or disruptions in the Gulf are often shared by all.

Many of the hardening and resiliency efforts undertaken at refineries also apply to pipeline terminals and retail outlets. To avoid redundant discussion, this study handles these assets jointly. Where specific measures apply to only refineries, pipelines, or terminals, such distinctions are made.

Petroleum Infrastructure Hardening

The hardening of petroleum infrastructure includes physical and structural improvements that make assets less vulnerable to the damaging effects of strong storms and hurricanes. Refineries, pipeline pump stations, terminals, retail outlets, corporate control centers, IT/communications, and supporting facilities are all examples of petroleum assets that benefit from storm hardening. Specific hardening activities that have been undertaken for petroleum infrastructure addressed in this study include:

- **Flood Protection**
  - **Building/strengthening berms, levees, and floodwalls**
  - **Elevating substations/control rooms/pump stations**[26]
  - **Relocating/constructing new facilities**
- **Wind Protection**
  - **Securing cooling towers**
  - **Improving tank integrity**
  - **Protecting cabling**

 - **Protecting retail outlets**
- **Modernization**
  - **Upgrading electrical systems** (e.g., with battery backup and uninterruptible power supplies)
  - **Installing/utilizing cogeneration**
  - **Enhancing IT and telecommunications** (adding Internet Protocol, phone lines, video-conferencing)
  - **Updating asset databases and tools**

Flood Protection

Flood damage is the costliest type of storm damage and results in the longest disruption duration for refineries, pipelines, and terminals. The risk of flooding is controlled by three main types of structural barriers:

- **Floodwalls**, which are often made of concrete or steel and are designed specifically to prevent flooding from storm surge.
- **Levees**, which are normally earthen structures designed to provide flood protection from seasonal high water. The word dike is used loosely by the industry, but usually refers to a levee-type structure.
- **Berms**, which, like levees, are usually earthen structures. Unlike levees, however, berms are designed specifically for spill containment, with flood protection as a secondary function.

Berms can be used to supplement levees, and are just as important for what they hold in (spills of hazardous materials) as for what they hold out (flood waters)[27] The company that owns or operates storage tanks, whether at a refinery or a tank farm, builds a berm around them. The dimensions can vary according to the engineering calculations of the amount of spill containment needed. Levees and floodwalls are erected by the U.S. Army Corps of Engineers (USACE) as well as by individual companies. Where these structures cannot be erected, petroleum companies have elevated critical facilities or relocate the facility above the floodplain.

Building/Strengthening Berms, Levees, and Floodwalls

Most flood walls were built decades ago to protect facilities located in the Gulf Coast. For example, USACE built the 15-foot-high concrete floodwall that protects the BP, Marathon, and Valero refineries, various chemical plants, and other facilities located near the Texas City port. The floodwall runs along most of the port, and has side slabs that can seal the rest when hurricanes hit.

Impacted facilities have requested USACE to build a five-foot vertical extension to the floodwall, raising it to 20 feet tall.[28]

USACE also built the Mississippi River levee system, which provides flood protection to 15 feet for refineries located near New Orleans. A $14 billion effort to reinforce it, along with the local floodwalls, is currently underway. By 2011, USACE expects to have a 350-mile system of levees, floodwalls, gates, and pumps providing five New Orleans parishes with 100-year protection.[29] In April 2009 USACE initiated a project to reinforce the entire length of the Port Arthur, Texas seawall for $8 million.[30]

Refiners built the floodwalls along the Houston Ship Channel and around Pascagoula to contain a 100-year storm surge. One refiner reported that a 12-foot-high, one-half-mile-long floodwall was erected in 2004 for under $4 million. Flood control projects constructed from earth, steel, and concrete are very expensive. ConocoPhillips has used a less expensive alternative called the HESCO Concertainer (see case study).

CASE STUDY: THE CONCERTAINER FLOODWALL

After Hurricane Katrina, the ConocoPhillips Alliance refinery in Belle Chasse, Louisiana undertook a project to provide interim flood protection using HESCO Concertainer units. These units are lightweight, portable cellular structures made of a welded mesh framework lined with geotextiles. Filled with sand, earth, or gravel, they provide flood protection. At the Belle Chasse refinery, the units were used to build floodwall structures that ranged from three feet high and three feet wide to eight feet high and six feet wide. The floodwall structures wrap around the entire refinery perimeter, including the tank farm, with secondary structures built around the most important control rooms and labs. In addition to providing flood protection, the HESCO units also function as a spill berm and security barrier. Approximately eight miles of HESCO Concertainer units were used in total. HESCO Concertainers can also be deployed atop levees or dikes to provide extra storm surge protection.

Source: HESCO web site: http://www.hesco.com/US_CIVIL/conoco.html, accessed April 22, 2010.

Flood barriers provide strong defenses, and at least one refiner credits its dike with a quicker post-hurricane restoration. Chevron's Pascagoula Refinery flooded in 1969 under Hurricane Camille, and again in 1998 under Hurricane

Georges. The destruction Georges caused was so severe that it took three months for the refinery to return to normal production levels. As a result, Chevron invested in a five-mile-long dike to protect the refinery. Despite significant local flooding from Hurricane Katrina in 2005, Chevron's refinery returned to normal production within six weeks.[31]

Although floodwaters have on occasion caused storage tanks to float off their foundations, direct flooding is not always the greatest challenge faced by refineries. In 2005, the Port Arthur levees were not topped, but the water supply on the Lower Natchez River was contaminated with salt water, making it useless for refinery processes. Another hazard is that water can become trapped inside the protective berms, exposing tanks and equipment to the corrosive effects of salt water.

Elevating Substations/Control Rooms/Pump Stations

Storm surge in 2005 damaged the control rooms and pump stations of numerous refineries and pipelines. When motors and electrical equipment sit in brackish water, even for a few hours, they suffer irreparable damage. One way to mitigate this risk is to elevate substations and control rooms so that they are situated above the likely flood level. In many cases, that level might be 15 - 25 feet above ground.

Although control room equipment is relatively light compared to other refinery equipment, elevating substations and control rooms is a costly measure that refiners consider very carefully before implementing. The expense varies significantly, depending on the size of the unit and other specifications, such as how much power is carried and how much wind and storm surge the unit is designed to withstand. According to one refiner, reported costs may range from $500-900 per square foot, based on the various attributes of the facility and the project design.

Some refineries have elevated their substations and control rooms as part of a larger modernization effort. While hurricanes might not have been the primary impetus for elevating the units, the storms provided lessons learned that guided decisions on how and where to situate the units.

Other refiners reported that in cases where control room equipment has not been elevated, it has been modified so it can be moved to safety in the event of an oncoming storm. At least one refiner upgraded storm water pumps and improved drainage.[32]

In general, pipeline operators handle the risk of flood damage differently than refiners. Because storm surge (with its corrosive salt water), and not heavy rain, is what creates the most serious flood risk, none of the pipeline operators reported any plans to elevate pump stations that are not located in flood zones.

Relocating/Constructing New Facilities

Petroleum companies located in the Gulf region face the reality that a direct hit from a major hurricane could make their facilities unsafe for the personnel needed for critical operations. In addition, local housing could become uninhabitable in a hurricane emergency, making it necessary for staff to stay elsewhere. Of secondary importance to human life, yet still essential, are the data network and control systems typically housed at a company's offices. Loss of these assets would be devastating to any company.

Having access to alternate facilities that are not only on higher ground, but in an entirely different region, may enhance a company's ability to continue critical operations during a hurricane and in its aftermath. An additional level of hardening can be provided by moving data and key software to remote facilities and constructing secondary control centers outside the Gulf region.

Several of the companies interviewed for this study reported that they have prepared alternate sites in parts of the United States that are not vulnerable to hurricanes, either for business operations, for the safekeeping of data systems, or for control centers. The rationale is that if their Gulf facilities become damaged or unsafe, they can continue essential functions. For example:

- BP has arranged for a 500-seat work site at its Chicago location for the use of displaced Houston staff so that they can continue critical operations in the event of a hurricane making landfall in the Gulf region.[33] The company has also moved data and key software to hardened data centers removed from the Gulf region.
- ExxonMobil has procured office space outside of hurricane-prone regions and has developed contingency plans for the relocation of key personnel in a hurricane emergency. Prior to Hurricane Ike's landing in 2008, essential employees were relocated to its Dallas office.[34] In addition, the company has planned for greater remote access to its network by increasing network capacity.
- Chevron Pipeline Co. has constructed a secondary control center in Midland Texas. This control center was put into service during Hurricanes Gustav and Ike in 2008.[35]

One alternative to creating auxiliary bases of operations in remote regions is the construction of safe rooms on the sites of Gulf Coast facilities. Safe rooms can be built to withstand the 250 mph winds and storm surge of a Category 5 hurricane. They are equipped with remote operation capability, and stocked with food, water, fuel, communications equipment, bedding, life rafts, and medical supplies. Although the study did not find any evidence indicating that any petroleum companies have plans for safe rooms, a number of them have been built by the Army Corps of Engineers for use by essential personnel at the water pumping stations in the New Orleans area.[36]

Wind Protection

Although hurricane-force winds are not as destructive to petroleum infrastructure as flooding, they still can cause severe damage to refineries, pipeline tank farms, and retail outlets. Any unit that is not underground is potentially vulnerable to the powerful lifting force of wind or the flying debris that comes with it. Especially prone to wind damage are cooling towers, empty storage tanks, and overhead or unprotected cabling.

Securing Cooling Towers

Cooling towers vary dramatically in size, depending on the required cooling load. They are often comparable to a two- to four-story structure, depending on whether the shrouds are taken into account. Hardening a cooling tower against hurricane damage is a major challenge. Construction is not durable; the shrouds of a cooling tower are typically made of fiberglass, which sit atop a timber or metal structure. If the fan blades inside the cooling tower are not secured, they can be launched from the tower, becoming airborne missiles. During Hurricane Rita, this mishap occurred at multiple refineries. Without a fan, the cooling tower is useless. For this reason, and because of the danger posed by flying fan blades, securing the fan blade is considered the most important component of storm-hardening a cooling tower.

Depending on the force of the wind, it can also damage the insulation packing inside a cooling tower. There are limitations to what can be done to protect the towers from this type of damage, because by design they have to allow air flow.

During the storms of 2005, the shrouds of numerous cooling towers were extensively damaged at refineries, chemical plants, and power stations (see Figure 5). In some cases, the damage was caused by launched fans. Aerial photographs of industrial facilities in the Port Arthur area after Hurricane Rita in 2005 revealed the extent of cooling tower failures (see Table 1).

Table 1. Cooling Tower Failures

Location	Facilities	Percent
Port Arthur	Refineries	50
Port Neches	Refineries	54
Bridge City	Power plants	44
Orange	Chemical plants	36

Source: Statistical analysis of aerial photographs of cooling tower damage and shroud failures in 2005 in NIST Technical Note 1476, *Performance of Physical Structures in Hurricane Katrina and Hurricane Rita: A Reconnaissance Report*, June 2006, http://www.bfrl.nist.gov/investigations/pubs/NIST_TN_1476_Exec Sum.pdf, accessed April 22, 2010.

Source: "Hurricanes Katrina and Rita: Implications for Hurricane Science and Engineering," http://www.nsf.gov/nsb/committees/archive/hurricane/1/sunder.pdf [BASF Fina Plant in Port Arthur, TX; photo from Christopher Letchford.

Figure 5. Damaged Cooling Tower Shroud.

Several of the refiners interviewed for this report have installed new braces to stop the fan blades from launching and damaging the shrouds. To prevent wind damage at its facilities, Valero has installed a Fan Lock to immobilize the fan blades in its cooling towers. This device locks mechanical equipment, including the fans, inside a cooling tower so that they will not rotate in high winds and damage the shrouds. [37]

Improving Tank Integrity

According to an estimate by one refiner, a complete rebuild of a destroyed storage tank could cost $65 - $80 per barrel, an estimate that includes tank and foundation construction, but not electrical and other expenses. Although total destruction of a tank is more likely to be caused by flooding than by wind, high winds can cause significant damage, and repairs can also be costly. Tanks are often insulated to keep contents at a particular temperature so that products can be easily transferred through piping and equipment. In 2005, extreme winds along the Gulf Coast ripped through the outer walls and roofs of both cylindrical storage tanks and LPG spheres, and damaged not only the outer shells, but also the insulation underneath.[38]

One relatively inexpensive way to harden storage tanks against wind damage is to install wind girders. These simple attachments are rings that encircle the storage tank, either singly or in a set of two. Depending on expected wind speeds (two are needed for winds greater than 120 mph), they reinforce the structural integrity of the tank, which helps to prevent collapse. If desired, wind girders can be designed as walkways for personnel access around the top of the tank (see Figure 6). Wind girders are available from various vendors, and are custom designed for each tank, based on size, anticipated wind load, and other customer requirements. Best practices for the selection and installation of wind girders are outlined in API 650, which is the American Petroleum Institute's standard that covers welded steel tanks for oil storage.[39]

Many of the tank operators reported that they have installed wind girders to their tanks. Costs vary on a tank-by-tank basis, but are generally cost-effective. One refiner reported spending $1.00 - $1.30 per barrel of tank capacity for larger tanks, some of which can hold 150,000- 200,000 barrels or more.

Source: ExxonMobil.

Figure 6. Wind Girders on Tanks.

Protecting Cabling

In a refinery, pipeline pumping station, or terminal, the component that is most vulnerable to wind damage may be the overhead cabling infrastructure. High winds can bring down electrical and instrument cables entirely or they can cause cables to touch, which can also result in damage.

Several hardening measures can be made within the refinery gate to address these risks. First, transmission cables can be insulated in such a way that if they do touch, there is no adverse effect. Secondly, electrical and instrument cables can be taken down from overhead towers and poles, and secured in an aboveground metal tray appropriately called a cable tray. A third alternative is to bury the cabling underground. Protective finishes are applied to cable before it is installed underground or in cable trays. In many cases, a combination of approaches can be used.

The National Electrical Manufacturers Association (NEMA) provides technical requirements concerning the construction, testing, and performance of metal cable tray systems.[40] At least two of the companies reported that they have installed cable trays to protect their lines from wind damage. One company specified that it had moved several miles of overhead wires to cable trays (see example in Figure 7).

Several other companies reported that they had "undergrounded" their cables; of those, at least one uses colored concrete to mark the exact placement of the cables.

Source: http://www.hydrocarbons-technology.com/projects/napanapa/, accessed April 14, 2010.

Figure 7. Cable Tray in a Refinery.

Protecting Retail Outlets

Functional fuel retail outlets are essential for a successful evacuation, an efficient recovery effort, and the timely return of the people who evacuated. Wind damage, however, can shut down these critical assets.

The canopies that are typically built to shelter the pumps have proven to be particularly vulnerable to hurricane winds. Canopy failure during recent hurricanes has been attributed to several causes.[41] In some cases, the pressure of the wind created hinges at the base of the columns. In other cases, the wind forced a foundation pullout. In still other cases, the wind caused breakage at the joints between the columns and the beams. These failures were primarily due to weak structural design; most of these canopies were supported by only a single row of columns. Maintenance lapses were also identified as the cause of certain canopy failures. Internal drainage can corrode the support structure, making it brittle and susceptible to wind damage.[42] When the canopy collapses, the pumps become inaccessible. One possible way to harden against canopy collapse is to build these structures with two rows of columns instead of one. According the National Institute of Standards and Technology, canopies with two rows of columns performed far better, with only a few failures identified.

In addition to the pump canopies, the store structures are also subject to debilitating wind damage. Many retail outlets have large windows, which can easily be broken by flying debris. When powerful winds are then allowed to enter the building, an upward force is created, which can threaten to lift the roof off of the structure. The simplest way to harden against this risk is to shutter the windows before the arrival of a storm. Historically, the most typical method for shuttering retail windows would be to board them up with sheets of plywood. Although this method is relatively inexpensive, it is also time-consuming and physically strenuous.

At least one fuel supplier has implemented a new shutter program for its retail stores. It provides the stores with hurricane shutters that are designed to allow for fast installation, which is managed on site by store personnel. These are portable shutters with connection systems permanently secured to the building. Shutters have been installed or stored on site at this supplier's company-owned stores on the Gulf Coast as of March 2010. The new shutters are installed much more quickly and easily than plywood boards, but they are costly. The company estimated a price tag in the range of $5,000-$12,000 per site, depending on size of the store.

Modernization

The petroleum industry expanded through the 1970s then went through a period of consolidation after the oil crises of 1973 and 1979. Industry consolidations initiated the sale or closure of redundant facilities, including terminal facilities, which led to reductions in inventory and system flexibility. Almost 50 refineries have closed over the last 20 years, and no major refineries have been built since 1976 although there has been a modest increase in capacity as a result of expansion of existing, larger refineries. To compensate for the aging infrastructure, companies are using updated electrical systems and modern advances such as efficient on-site cogeneration and upgraded technology in refinery and pipeline control rooms. Companies are using new technologies, such as cathodic protection which reduces corrosion, to extend the life of their storage facilities.

Upgrading Electrical Systems

The electrical system is a vital component of petroleum refining and distribution. It is also the part of the refinery that is most susceptible to damage from hurricanes, usually caused by flooding from storm surge. One way that companies have hardened their facilities is by upgrading the electrical systems to make them more efficient and less susceptible to damage. Improvements include installing new or additional substations, upgrading power distribution systems, installing new breakers and transformers, and using advanced electrical power monitoring systems. Some of the companies interviewed have also installed new high voltage transmission lines into their refineries. Other facilities on the Gulf Coast have installed permanent backup generators for use in administrative buildings, control centers, and emergency operations centers to support a safe shutdown and recovery. These generators are designed to support personnel and distribution systems at control centers and are not meant to run the refining equipment.

Some companies have reported using uninterruptible power supplies (UPS) and battery backup systems at refinery control rooms. A UPS is a device that uses energy storage technologies to provide emergency power during an outage. The main function of a UPS is to facilitate an orderly, rather than sudden, shutdown of computers or process equipment at the facility. UPS systems also aid in the transition to an alternate power source. Most battery-enabled UPS systems are designed to provide power for 15 minutes, or slightly longer, until power is restored or a backup power source is brought online.

However, one refiner reported the use of a UPS that can provide sufficient power to operate the control room for 24 hours without grid power. Uninterrupted power is essential in part because computer data must be saved before a lengthy outage since preserving data aids in the recovery process. Even a momentary disruption can damage equipment, data, or processes in control rooms. Therefore, a facility will often "float" on the UPS, operating directly off of the UPS battery system while the UPS is constantly charged by the grid.[43]

Installing/Utilizing Cogeneration

Twenty-five Gulf Coast refineries have co-located electric generation facilities.[44] The industrial gas plant beside the refinery may be the owner/operator, or the electric utility may be the operator, but the majority of generation facilities are owned and operated by the refinery.

The vast majority of these power-generating units – those at 21 of the 25 refineries – are cogeneration systems.[45] A cogeneration system uses "a common energy source to produce both electricity and steam for other uses, resulting in increased fuel efficiency."[46] Most refineries have multiple units that range in size from 4 MW to 285 MW and generate an average of 50 MW.[47] A Lake Charles, Louisiana refinery is home to the region's oldest co-located electric units. Two of its three power units entered service in 1942. Many of the larger units in the region (those greater than 100 MW) came online in the 1990s or 2000s.

Cogeneration facilities may not make a refinery self-sufficient. Thirteen of the 25 refineries consume more electricity than their co-located power units can generate, i.e., they are "net purchasers." Only 12 of the 25 co-located power facilities produce more electricity than the refineries demand, i.e., they are "net suppliers."

It would seem, intuitively, that a refinery with an on-site source of power would be better- equipped to deal with a natural disaster than a refinery that depends on an external source for electricity. All of the interviewed refiners had cogeneration in one or more Gulf Coast facilities but none attributed a faster recovery or hardened operation to their cogeneration plant. Furthermore, an analysis of several Gulf Coast refineries' responses to recent storms – Hurricane Rita in 2005 and Hurricane Ike in 2008 – yielded inconclusive results. The analysis considered the six refineries in the Port Arthur/Lake Charles region as reported daily in OE Situation Reports (see Table 2). Two weeks after Hurricane Rita made landfall in 2005, all six refineries remained shut down. Two weeks after Hurricane Ike made landfall in 2008, refineries with cogeneration fared only marginally better. Refineries with sufficient cogeneration capacity to be a net supplier recovered more quickly in 2008 than in 2005, but that may be due to less damage to Lake Charles. Cogeneration facilities existed in both years, but perhaps they have been improved. At least one refiner indicated that it installed new circuit breakers, new cabling, new transformers, and two 2-MW portable generators for the capability to start up the cogeneration plant.

Enhancing IT and Telecommunications

Hurricanes often severely limit or completely eliminate a company's ability to communicate critical information both internally and to other organizations and employees. Several companies have enhanced their IT and telecommunications infrastructure in preparation for storms to help ensure that communications remain operational in emergencies.

After Hurricane Katrina, Valero set up 20 satellite phones and about 40 cellular and radio phones to communicate between its San Antonio, Texas refinery and its St. Charles and Krotz Springs refineries in southern Louisiana. In addition, Valero set up connections in San Antonio to an Internet Protocol (IP) phone switch at the St. Charles facility to support voice communications. Valero also installed satellite communications that enabled it to communicate with 14 retail stations located between New Orleans and Lafayette, as well as with three in the Shreveport area.[48]

Table 2. Status of Refineries in Port Arthur/Lake Charles Two Weeks after Hurricanes

Refiner	Location	Cogeneration	Rita (2005)	Ike (2005)
Calcasieu	Lake Charles, LA	Net Supplier	Shut down	Operating 2 days
Shell (Motiva)	Port Arthur, TX	Net Supplier	Shut down	Reduced 2 days
ExxonMobil	Beaumont, TX	Net Supplier	Shut down	Shut down
Citgo	Lake Charles, LA	Net Purchaser	Shut down	Reduced 14 days
Valero (Premcor)	Port Arthur, TX	Net Purchaser	Shut down	Shut down
Total	Port Arthur, TX	None	Shut down	Restarting

Sources: OE/ISER Situation Reports, EIA-861 Annual Report.

Other companies reported installing IP phone systems and additional analog phone lines to serve as backup. Cellular carrier and radio transmission antennas were also added to some company buildings, and satellite communications have also been employed. One company reported the installation of wiring to allow handheld satellite phones from an operations building during severe weather. Another reported the use of small portable satellite communications systems that can be easily deployed where necessary.

As part of ExxonMobil's storm preparation they have secured the use of satellite communications and increased the number of people who can connect to their system simultaneously.[49]

Installing Asset Databases and Tools

The ability to monitor critical facilities, such as pipeline networks, and reestablish production quickly in the event of damage is a key component of hurricane preparation and recovery for the petroleum industry. One way that companies monitor their assets is through the use of Supervisory Control and Data Acquisition (SCADA) systems. SCADA systems are computer- based industrial control systems used to collect data and exercise control from a remote location. They are used in the pipeline industry to collect data from sensors in real time and relay that information to controllers. Controllers can then remotely operate pipeline equipment such as valves and pumps.[50] Satellite technology is frequently used to provide high quality connectivity for SCADA applications in the pipeline industry since it provides reliable communications, even in harsh environments.

BP uses a SCADA system with state-of-the-art satellite communications, complemented in some areas by terrestrial circuits, radio links, and dial backup phone lines. Every seven to 10 seconds it gathers more than 38,000 data points from over 300 locations, showing changes in fluid levels, pressure, flow, temperatures, gravity, alarms, security, pump speeds, hazardous atmosphere, and other critical readings. The general location of pipeline irregularities can most often be determined relatively quickly by a skilled pipeline controller who can then close valves, isolate problems and make repairs.[51]

The use of Geographic Information Systems (GIS) is becoming more common in the petroleum industry as a tool for analyzing and displaying infrastructure data. For example, GIS programs can be utilized to monitor the condition and flow of pipelines during and after a hurricane. One of the most difficult jobs after a hurricane is damage assessment. GIS tools can play an important role in short-term recovery efforts by mapping damaged facilities, the type and amount of damage, and priorities for action.[52] At least one company, ExxonMobil, uses a GIS-based generator tracking system to monitor the location and status of deployed portable generators.[53]

Updates have also been made to rules that regulate the operation of control rooms, where this technology is most often located and operated. DOT/PHMSA administers Control Room Management (CRM) rules that apply to operators of pipeline facilities with a controller who monitors and operates all or part of a pipeline facility through a SCADA system. Each operator must follow written control room management procedures as detailed by the rule. The amended rule, effective February 2010, ensures that control systems are matched to human capabilities and limitations, including fatigue management. The amendments are a result of National Transportation Safety Board (NTSB) investigations into actual pipeline accidents, during which the NTSB identified key root causes and then proposed five areas for potential improvement:[54]

- Controller display graphics
- Alarm management
- Controller training
- Controller fatigue
- Leak detection

The new regulations contain specific requirements for operators to design and operate their SCADA system to take specific account of these improvement areas and what is needed by the controller to properly do the job of keeping things operating safely and responsibly.

Petroleum companies can draw upon databases and tools made available by regulatory agencies. In Texas, for instance, the Railroad Commission maintains a comprehensive critical infrastructure/key resources database of above- and underground storage, including the Strategic Petroleum Reserve, and meter and pump stations.[55] The Texas Commission on Environmental Quality (TCEQ) developed and maintains interactive databases on environmental emergency, discharge, spill, or air release from refineries and above ground storage tanks.[56]

Petroleum Infrastructure Resiliency

Improving the resiliency of petroleum infrastructure involves activities that enable refineries, pipelines, terminals, and retail outlets to continue operating despite damage. It also involves increasing the facility's capacity to return to normal operations rapidly if outages do occur. Petroleum companies may take resiliency measures as general precautions, or they may take them in preparation for specific storm events.

General Readiness

General readiness activities are geared toward preparing refineries, pipelines, terminals, and retail outlets to recover quickly from damage from flooding, extreme winds, and other impacts from storms. Because such activities are considered effective against any storm event, they may occur before hurricane season or throughout the year. They include:

- **Conducting hurricane preparedness planning and training**
- **Complying with inspection protocols**
- **Improving employee communications and tracking**
- **Installing redundant communications**
- **Procuring mobile command vehicles**
- **Purchasing/leasing portable generators**
- **Pre-positioning and pre-wiring portable generators**
- **Securing alternate sources of gas supplies**

Conducting Hurricane Preparedness Planning and Training

A hurricane preparation plan is the primary component of any petroleum company's overall storm resiliency. Each plan lays out the steps necessary to minimize the potential impact to the facility from an approaching storm. Typically, plans are reviewed for effectiveness and updated after each hurricane.

The refinery and pipeline operators interviewed for this study all confirmed that they maintain confidential hurricane preparedness plans. The companies would not share their plans with DOE, but they do share information with members of their trade organizations, the American Petroleum Institute (API), the National Petrochemical & Refiners Association (NPRA), and the Association of Oil Pipe Lines (AOPL). API and AOPL are not as focused on hurricane planning as NPRA, which compiled the lessons learned from the 2005 hurricane season into a planning and crisis response guide for operators of refineries and petrochemical plants. The NPRA *Hurricane Security Operations*[57] addresses both pre-hurricane planning and recovery operations, and outlines specific steps to best prepare for a hurricane (see Table 3).

Table 3. Typical Petroleum Industry Emergency Response Plan Elements

- Establish an emergency management team
  - Appoint a senior official as team lead
  - Participate in daily calls
  - Set roles and responsibilities for responders
- Assess facility security
  - Identify critical sites that require security
  - Issue company badges and authorization letters to first responders
  - Detail the steps to secure critical sites, gates, and equipment
  - Itemize and stock supplies and equipment, including portable generators
- Enhance logistics
  - Provide security supplies and equipment to ride-out staff
  - Prepare for transportation needs, e.g., fill vehicle tanks, strategically position vehicles, prepare for convoy needs, obtain magnetic signs with company logo
  - Stock extra chains, padlocks, battery-operated lights, and spare parts
- Ensure reliable communications options
  - Incorporate all modes, e.g., landline, cell, satellite, walkie-talkies, blackberries
  - Authorize Wireless Priority Service on key cell phones and Government Emergency Telecommunications Service (GETS) cards
  - Update and distribute paper copies of contact information
- Coordinate with key personnel
  - Educate employees to prepare for extended shelter-in-place periods
  - Secure temporary lodging for displaced employees and their families
  - Have medical personnel on-site for first aid and immunizations
  - Set up hot-line or website for employee status reports
  - Arrange cash payroll and dispense emergency funds
- Maintain relations with communities and governmental agencies
  - Evaluate in advance governmental transportation permit requirements
  - Assess emergency procedures, evacuation, and search-and-rescue plans
  - Refuel State emergency vehicles and share food and water to win cooperation
  - Meet with electric utilities providing power to key assets

Source: Adapted from NPRA, Hurricane Security Operations, May 31, 2006, and ExxonMobil, What we do when storms hit hard, http://www.exxonmobil.com/corporate/news_features_20090601_storm_prep.aspx, accessed May 18, 2010.

ExxonMobil has extensive hurricane preparedness plans that include procedures for preparation, response, and recovery. Approximately ten days before projected hurricane landfall, personnel and equipment preparations are started, including travel out of potentially impacted areas.[58] Preemptive inspections and preparations take place within approximately seven days from landfall. About four days from landfall, coastal refineries that may be affected by the storm are shut down if necessary, or shifted to "safe park" mode, a reduced-output state that helps conserve crude oil and other key supplies that may be interrupted by the storm.[59]

Shell and Motiva also follow a phased approach for storm season preparations. In advance of a storm, they consider all critical plant functions, including computing services, communications, utilities, crude oil deliveries, petrochemical feedstocks, product distribution, health, safety, and environment. They have on duty at all times a workforce that can operate and maintain a facility safely, or if need be, shut down the units in a safe and controlled manner. They also have designated teams that stay behind during a storm. These teams represent a mix of expertise, including logistics, security, site supervision, and emergency medical skills.[60]

Chevron's Pascagoula refinery has ten medical first responders and 25 nationally certified Emergency Medical Technicians on staff for medical emergencies. They also have an Emergency Response Team that includes 80 employee volunteers who complete 150 hours of specialized training each year to respond to emergency situations.[61] ExxonMobil's Baytown refinery and Chemical Plant have a similar arrangement with 80 emergency response volunteers who are required to complete a minimum of 80 hours of training per year.[62]

Complying with Inspection Protocols

Regular inspections of petroleum refineries, terminals, and pipelines indicate whether equipment is properly functioning before a hurricane strikes. These inspections often occur during maintenance or turnarounds.[63] Even though not every unit at a refinery is impacted during each turnaround, refineries are typically shut down (totally or partially) for maintenance that is scheduled at least one or two years in advance, and can last one to four weeks.[64]

Refinery, pipeline, and terminal operators follow inspection-related codes, standards, and recommended practices developed and published by API. Other organizations, e.g., the American National Standards Institute (ANSI) and the International Organization for Standardization (ISO), are encouraged to adopt API's codes, standards, and recommended practices.

The selected API codes, standards, and recommended practices in Table 4 address inspection at refineries, pipelines, and terminals. API sponsors an Individual Certification Program to certify inspectors responsible for enforcing Codes 510 and 570 and Standard 653.[65]

Most petroleum companies follow API's recommended practices and standards regarding inspections. Inspections of aboveground petroleum product storage tanks (exceeding 50,000 gallon capacity) are defined by API Standard 650, "Welded Steel Tanks for Oil Storage." The frequency and specifics of the inspections vary greatly based on the contents of the tank, the corrosion rate, location, local regulations, and other factors. Normally, the schedule of inspections is set up at the time of construction and a record is kept of inspections, including any modifications, repairs, or changes of service.[66]

- Routine in-service external inspections are conducted monthly
- Turnaround inspections are conducted by an API-certified inspector at least every five years, and look for leaks, bulges, corrosion, settlement, and breaks in coating and insulation, as well as monitor cathodic protection systems
- Internal inspections of the bottom plates for corrosion and leaks are conducted at least every 20 years

There is very little regulatory oversight of hardening and resiliency efforts at refineries and petroleum pipelines. The Federal Energy Regulatory Commission (FERC) oversees interstate pipeline movements, but is more focused on the pricing and monopolization of the market. The PHMSA maintains more than 75 full-time pipeline inspectors in the field to inspect interstate pipelines and enforce compliance with Federal pipeline safety regulations. However, the majority of pipeline inspections are carried out by State inspectors who work for State regulatory agencies.[67]

For pipelines, inspections are dictated by Federal law, which requires that rights-of-way are visually inspected at least 26 times a year either by walking, driving, or flying the course, or by other appropriate means.[68] At intervals not exceeding five years, operators must also inspect each crossing under a navigable waterway to determine the condition of the crossing.[69] Pipeline operators may enforce their own, more stringent inspection programs. At least one operator, BP, performs manned aerial inspections of both rights-of-way and pipelines 52 times a year.[70] They are currently investigating the possibility of performing multiple inspections per week using unmanned aerial drones.

Table 4. Selected API Inspection-Related Codes, Standards, and Practices

API No.	Title
Code 510	Pressure Vessel Inspection Code: In-Service Inspection, Rating, Repair, and Alteration
Code 570	Piping Inspection Code: In-Service Inspection, Rating, Repair, and Alteration of Piping Systems
RP 571	Damage Mechanisms Affecting Fixed Equipment in the Refining Industry
RP 572	Inspection Practices for Pressure Vessels
RP 574	Inspection Practices for Piping System Components
RP 575	Guidelines and Methods for Inspection of Existing Atmospheric and Low-Pressure Storage Tanks
RP 576	Inspection of Pressure-Relieving Devices
RP 577	Welding Inspection and Metallurgy
RP 580	Risk-Based Inspection
RP 581	Risk-Based Inspection Technology
Std 598	Valve Inspection and Testing
Std 650	Welded Tanks for Oil Storage: Tank Inspection, Repair, Alteration, and Reconstruction
RP 651	Cathodic Protection of Aboveground Petroleum Storage Tanks
Std 653	Aboveground Storage Tank Inspection, Repair, Alteration, and Reconstruction
Std 2610	Design, Construction, Operation, Maintenance and Inspection of Terminal and Tank Facilities

Notes: RP = recommended practice; Std = Standard

Source: Adapted from API, Standards, http://www.api.org/Standards/, accessed May 18, 2010.

Improving Employee Communications and Tracking

All of the refinery and pipeline operators interviewed for this study indicated that the safety of their employees was paramount. These companies provide shelter, food, supplies, and communications services to assist employees and speed recovery. They have numerous methods of keeping track of their employees and communicating with them before, during, and after a hurricane. These methods include websites, hotlines, and media channels, and are aimed at ensuring employee safety and enabling a quick and coordinated response after a storm has passed.

Marathon assisted more than 650 employees and their families impacted by Hurricane Katrina through donations of food, water, generators, and other household items. In addition, they set up temporary housing for employees whose homes had been damaged or destroyed and provided employees with interest-free loans up to $10,000 to assist in their recovery efforts.[71] Marathon has since developed a website, www.MarathonCares.com, which serves as an employee emergency communication center and provides timely information to employees and family members in the event of an emergency. The system also provides critical contact information for the Corporate Emergency Response Team, refinery emergency hotlines, and other employee assistance contacts.[72]

ExxonMobil has instituted an automated employee tracking system that can deliver two-way, interactive communications via phone and e-mail to ascertain the safety and well-being of employees in an emergency situation. The Automated Tracking System stores employee emergency contact information and provides a toll-free number for employees to report their status following an emergency.[73]

Shell and Motiva work with the media and other communication channels to instruct employees not to report to work when conditions may be unsafe.[74]

Chevron provides a toll-free Gulf Coast Employee Hotline for employees and contractors, their families, and friends that can be used to report the whereabouts of employees or contractors. In emergency situations, employees and contractors are required to call their plant's toll-free emergency information number for recorded status updates on plant shutdown, reporting back to work, plant restart, and other critical information.[75]

In Texas, the Railroad Commission assumes responsibility for notifying the public of incoming hurricanes starting 120 hours in advance of potential landfall. It releases public service announcements on radio and other media, and initiates preparedness and response actions.[76]

Also after Katrina, the State of Illinois, working with the State of Louisiana, contributed a number of Ground Control Magellan Mobile Satellite Internet Systems (MSS) to provide communications for Katrina relief efforts. A large tent was erected that housed 30 laptops that were simultaneously connected to the MSS's wireless networks. Each workstation had Voice- Over-Internet-Protocol capabilities and videoconference capacity via web cam (see Figure 8).[77]

During Hurricane Rita, PHMSA facilitated efforts to obtain temporary housing through FEMA for pipeline personnel in the Gulf area. Temporary housing was provided in the form of mobile homes and trailers.[78]

Installing Redundant Communications

During hurricane emergencies, landlines often fail and wireless systems can become congested. Because hurricane preparation, response, and recovery depends on a company's ability to communicate with personnel and other business units, the installation of secondary or redundant communication channels is widely regarded as an essential element of hurricane readiness. When landlines fail, companies can use secondary cellular networks, satellite communications, internet voice communications services, and priority calling capabilities to ensure that communications with company personnel and local and Federal government agencies are maintained. A number of refiners store satellite phones in corporate offices, delivering them to the potentially impacted facility before a hurricane makes landfall.

Almost every refiner and pipeline operator indicated that their employees use two priority calling services made available by the National Communications System:

- Government Emergency Telecommunications Service (GETS)
- Wireless Priority Service (WPS)

GETS provides priority treatment for authorized users to ensure a higher rate of call completion during periods of outages or congestion resulting from disasters. GETS utilizes local networks provided by Local Exchange Carriers and wireless providers, major long-distance networks and international services, and government leased networks. GETS is accessed through a universal access number plus a PIN that is authenticated to guarantee priority service.[79] Key personnel work with government officials to obtain a GETS emergency card. During Hurricanes Katrina and Rita, the National Communications System issued over 1,000 new GETS cards and over 40,000 GETS calls were made in the ensuing recovery period. Over 5,500 GETS calls were made by emergency response officials in Louisiana alone, allowing them to complete calls that otherwise would not have gone through due to congestion and outages resulting from the damage to the infrastructure.[80]

WPS is the wireless counterpart of GETS. It provides priority treatment for calls made from cell phones during periods of wireless network congestion. WPS is an add-on feature subscribed on a per-cell phone basis that works with existing cell phones in WPS-enabled cellular networks. WPS provides priority for emergency calls through a combination of special cellular network features and the same high probability of completion features used by GETS: WPS calls wait in queue for the next available channel if a channel is not immediately available.[81]

Procuring Mobile Command Vehicles

Mobile command vehicles are used in many sectors of the economy. The vehicles purchased or leased by refiners and pipeline operators are often similar to those ordered by local governments (county, parish, or city), especially in areas where refineries and terminals are located (see Figure 9). The vehicles are equipped with office computers and printers, satellite phone and internet, emergency lighting, and other supplies.

Source: http://www.groundcontrol.com/katrina.htm, accessed May 5, 2010.

Figure 8. Communications Tent.

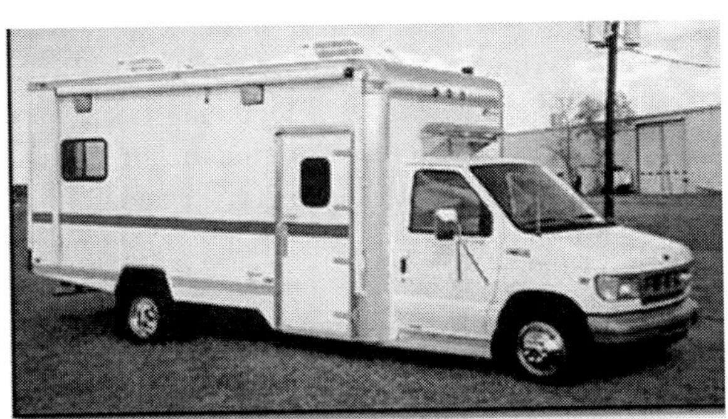

Source: Clegg Industries, built for Chevron, http://www.cleggind.com/specialty vehicles/chevronrefinery.html, accessed May 22, 2010.

Figure 9. Incident Command Center.

Refineries have had their own fire and rescue vehicles for decades. The need for mobile command centers sprouted in the late 1990s when hurricanes flooded refineries and terminals, making it impossible for operators to access their control rooms and offices. Some mobile command centers occupy a small truck.[82] The fire brigade at the ConocoPhillips Lake Charles refinery includes two similar command vehicles and an enclosed rescue trailer.[83] Larger trailer-based mobile command centers are used by local governments in the Gulf region (see Figure 10).

Most of the pipeline operators interviewed (especially those managing large terminals) have mobile command centers in addition to a variety of trucks for fire suppression. At least one, Kinder Morgan, has a centrally stationed communications trailer equipped with satellite telephones and portable generators.[84]

Purchasing or Leasing Portable Generators

The loss of grid electricity at refineries, pipeline pumping stations, terminals, and other petroleum industry facilities during a hurricane can severely limit or shut down operations at a facility, even if the facility itself is not damaged. Without power, refineries cannot continue to operate, and petroleum products cannot be moved through pipelines. During electrical outages, therefore, petroleum companies rely on portable generators to provide electricity to critical facilities until grid power can be restored. Purchasing portable generation equipment, or leasing it in advance, ensures that there will be no delays in procuring reliable power when a hurricane approaches.

Portable generators are available in a range of sizes and capacities, from retail scale units (~35 kW) to large 2-MW trailer-mounted units (see Figure 11). Even the large 2-MW mobile generators cannot provide enough electricity to power an entire refinery. However, these generators are used to operate the data control center, critical IT facilities, or maintain selected units in idle mode (as opposed to shutdown) for a faster recovery. In addition, two 2-MW units can power a small 2,500-horsepower (hp) pump station, maintaining pipeline operations. The small portable generators are primarily for retail outlets. These units are typically pre-wired to enable rapid start-up.

The National Fire Protection Association Standard 110 "Standard for Emergency and Standby Power Systems" provides guidance regarding the amount of fuel to maintain onsite for a portable generator, which may be required to operate for up to 96 hours, or possibly more.[85]

Economic considerations determine whether refiners and pipeline operators choose to purchase or lease portable generators. All of the Gulf

Coast refiners interviewed purchase and/or lease large mobile generators. A new 2-MW trailer-mounted unit costs approximately $0.5 million. This is the delivered price of the generator; necessary accessories (e.g., cables, batteries, fuel tanks) must be purchased, which will raise the installed price over $1 million.[86]

ConocoPhillips' Alliance refinery in New Orleans leases generators for use as backup power for water extraction pumps. The pumps are located at one of the lowest ground areas of the refinery and are designed to redirect storm water away from the plant and refinery equipment. The setup includes two 2-MW trailer-mounted Kohler generators providing redundant backup power to four 390-hp pumps. In addition, two transformers and a motor control center are wired to the generators. The full setup requires 3,600 feet of cable. The configuration is designed so that two pumps can run entirely on one generator, or all four pumps can share the electrical load between the two generators.[87]

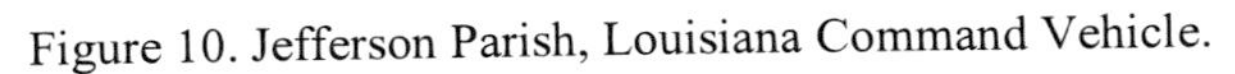
Source: www.jeffparish.net/index.cfm?DocID=6253, accessed May 11, 2010.

Figure 10. Jefferson Parish, Louisiana Command Vehicle.

Source: ExxonMobil, April 2010.

Figure 11. Large Mobile Generators.

All but one of the interviewed pipeline operators indicated that they lease rather than buy their mobile generators, either before the hurricane season starts or after a storm makes landfall. One operator noted that there was little benefit to leasing large generators and has stopped this practice. The experience of this operator was that it incurred significant expenses hooking up the leased generators, and in the end the effort did not benefit the movement of product up the pipeline. From the perspective of this operator, an area power outage means that there is no refinery production or stock drawdown to keep the pipeline operational, which makes leasing a portable generator not cost-effective.

Colonial Pipeline is the one pipeline operator that purchased generators. To avoid a recurrence of the shutdowns it experienced during the 2005 hurricane season, Colonial purchased 12 trailer- mounted Mitsubishi portable generators, seven transformers, and miles of associated cabling in 2006.[88] Colonial prepares for hurricane season by completing maintenance and testing to ensure generators are road-worthy and that contractors are lined up to install and start up the units (see case study).

Case Study: Colonial Pipeline's Experience with Mobile Generators

Setting up mobile generators and transformers can be daunting, particularly when laying 6,000 feet of cable for six generators in wet, soggy area (see Figure 12):

- 30 cables (each 140 feet long) between each generator and transformer
- Six cables (each 300 feet long) between each transformer and the main bus

In 2008, Colonial Pipeline activated these generators multiple times. On September 3, 2008, Colonial started to set up six mobile generators at its blacked-out Baton Rouge, Louisiana pump station. It took 48 hours and over 100 Colonial staff and contractors to install, wire and start-up the units. Tear-down of the site started on September 8, 2008, after grid power was restored.

Source: Colonial Pipeline, 2009 Tulane Engineering Forum.

Figure 12. Portable Generator Cabling.

Source: Colonial Pipeline, 2009 Tulane Engineering Forum.

Figure 13. Portable Generators in Texas.

On September 14, 2008, Colonial Pipeline organized a convoy to move eight generators, two trailers of transformers, two container trailers holding cable, and other equipment from Baton Rouge to their Hebert Station and Port Arthur, Texas facilities, which were blacked out by Ike (see Figure 13). Over 100 Colonial personnel and contractors were involved in the generator deployment to Texas. The generators ran intermittently for a week, stopping when fuel supplies ran out. The generators and auxiliary equipment are stored at the Kola pumping station in Collins, Mississippi, where they sit ready to be deployed again.

Source: Patrick J. Mihelick, "Colonial Pipeline, One Pipeline Company's Response to Hurricanes Gustav and Ike," 2009 Tulane Engineering Forum, http://www.tulane. edu/~sse/FORUM_2009/program/, accessed January 20, 2010.

Pre-positioning and Pre-wiring Portable Generators

Another hurricane resiliency practice is to strategically pre-position portable generators in locations that are beyond the storm track, but in close proximity to the affected facilities to allow rapid deployment. Smaller portable generators are pre-wired at critical communications and IT facilities. Companies will also procure substation and transformer components before a storm arrives so that any damaged equipment can be restored to normal operating conditions rapidly. Four interviewed companies indicated that they have pre-wired critical sections of their refineries and pipeline terminals.

Positioning generators to power key service stations along evacuation routes is another element of hurricane resiliency planning. These stations provide critical fuel and supplies to residents and responders before and after a storm evacuation. Even undamaged retail stations may require emergency power to remain open.

All petroleum companies that operate retail stores on the Gulf Coast and in the Southeast indicated that they have pre-wired some of their service stations. In addition, Shell has pre-wired all critical terminals in its South Distribution Region for portable generators and transformers so that deliveries can be quickly restored following a hurricane. Shell has also pre-positioned portable generators in safe areas in the Gulf region to ensure rapid deployment.[89]

ExxonMobil owns one of the industry's largest fleet of small portable generators (see Figure 14). The company has positioned 90 small mobile generators in four storage facilities within 200 miles of the Gulf Coast. In addition, it plans to install 10 permanent generators at various locations throughout Florida.[90] ExxonMobil retail stations are pre-wired for portable generators to facilitate rapid start-up and operation. The generators are loaded on flatbed trucks and are ready for distribution well before a hurricane makes landfall. They are big enough to run all aspects of a retail station, and with pre-wiring can power a facility within 24 hours of delivery.[91]

Florida has enacted legislation requiring retail stations within a half mile of evacuation routes to be equipped with a generator to power the pumps. In addition, all owners of more than ten retail stations in a Florida county must, within 24 hours of an emergency declaration, have a generator installed at 10 percent of their retail stations. All portable generators must be stored within the State or within 250 miles of the station.[92] Currently all 970 retail stations covered by the law either have a generator or are wired to accept one. In addition, the law requires new or remodeled retail stations to be pre- wired for generators regardless of their distance from an evacuation route. So far, 207 of those retail stations can run on generator power. It was reported that costs for converting a retail station's wiring to handle a generator can range from $15,000 to $20,000.[93]

Securing Alternate Sources of Gas Supplies

Refineries require substantial amounts of natural gas and industrial gases for regular operations. Natural gas is used in boilers to produce steam and hot water for the distillation process, which initiates product refining. Refineries located along the Gulf Coast obtain their natural gas supplies directly from gas pipelines in the Gulf of Mexico, where offshore oil platforms produce associated natural gas while extracting crude oil. The wet gas is dried at gas processing units on the coast, and then piped to refineries. When hurricanes arrive in the Gulf of Mexico, platforms are evacuated and production is reduced and/or shut in, cutting off the refineries' supply of natural gas. Some refiners have begun to contract with inland gas pipelines (obtaining direct hookups to natural gas pipelines) to guarantee natural gas supplies, even during hurricane staging periods.

Industrial gases – hydrogen, nitrogen, oxygen – are used throughout refining processes:

- Hydrogen is a necessary component of hydrocracking, which uses catalysts and hydrogen to convert fuel oil into light products. Hydrotreating requires hydrogen to remove sulfur and nitrogen from products.[94]
- Nitrogen is used to purge equipment, tanks, and pipelines of dangerous vapors and gases (e.g., during restart and after completing a pipeline transfer operation or ending a production run) and to maintain an inert and protective atmosphere in tanks storing flammable liquids. Nitrogen suppresses flammability by reducing oxygen levels to a point below which combustion is possible.[95]
- Oxygen is used to enrich the air feed to catalytic cracking regenerators and sulfur recovery units, which increases capacity of the units. Oxygen is also used to regenerate catalysts in refineries.[96]

To guarantee access to supply of these gases, some refiners have co-located their refineries with industrial gas facilities, or incorporated industrial gas plants in their expansion designs. In one such case, an Air Liquide plant is located adjacent to Valero's Corpus Christi refinery, delivering industrial gases to refining, petrochemical, and steel plants in the vicinity. Air Liquide operates

1,800 miles of pipeline along the Texas and Louisiana Coast, delivering industrial gases to more than 130 petrochemical and refinery customers.[97] The expansion of the Marathon Garyville refinery includes a new hydrogen facility and hydrogen pipeline.[98] In at least one case, the industrial gas plant is integrated with a cogeneration plant that provides electricity to the refinery. The new Air Products hydrogen and cogeneration facility, inaugurated in 2007, is adjacent to the Valero Port Arthur refinery.[99]

Industrial gases, particularly nitrogen, are required for start-up of critical refinery production units. When industrial gas plants sustain damage (e.g., Air Products Michoud plant in New Orleans from Hurricane Katrina), some refiners have had to obtain many trucks' worth of bottled hydrogen and nitrogen in order to start their facilities. Other refiners have contracted with third parties to increase the reliability of supply when the refinery is restarting. Motiva, for example, has commissioned an 85-mile, 20-inch pipeline to transport hydrogen from Air Liquide's Bayport plant to Motiva's Port Arthur refinery. Construction of the line was slated to have been finished in the first quarter of 2010.[100]

Storm-Specific Readiness

Resiliency activities undertaken to address a specific storm help speed recovery. They include:

- **Maintaining minimum tank volumes**
- **Wrapping/protecting pumps & motors**
- **Facilitating employee evacuation and reentry**
- **Coordinating priority restoration and waivers**

Source: ExxonMobil, April 2010.

Figure 14. Portable Generators for Retail Stations.

Maintaining Minimum Tank Volumes

Above-ground storage tanks are at particular risk during storm surge flooding since they can actually float off their foundations when spill-containment areas became flooded with water. One method that companies use to prevent tank movement is to ensure that an adequate amount of product is in the tank prior to a storm. This adds weight and stability to the tank and can prevent it from floating off its platform.

At least four of the companies reported taking steps to ensure a minimum volume of product is in their storage tanks before a storm arrives. Keeping product in the storage tanks at terminals prior to a storm also serves to reduce the possibility of product being stranded at a refinery if an outage occurs. The companies reported that it is necessary to begin very early before a storm to secure enough product to fill the tanks, since there can be competition among petroleum companies and emergency responders as a storm approaches. It is especially difficult when hurricanes strike in close succession, as occurred in 2005 and again in 2008, because it is more difficult to procure product after a storm. Some companies reported filling tanks completely prior to a storm. One company reported filling tanks ¾ full. It was also reported that another advantage of filling tanks prior to a storm is that a full tank is more rigid and less susceptible to wind damage, especially if wind girders are not installed.

The API Standard 650, "Welded Steel Storage Tanks," recommends special consideration in areas where tanks are subject to flooding of the berm, dike, or other secondary containment area when the tank is empty of liquid. Flooding of the containment area can uplift the tank, and imposes hydrostatic pressure against the outside of the tank shell. Normally, the amount of water that collects is not sufficient to impose significant pressure, but the height of water can be enough to "balloon" the bottom of the tank. One practical method commonly used to mitigate the risk of this type of damage is to maintain a minimum liquid level inside the tank that is high enough, considering the relative specific gravities of the liquids inside and outside the tank, to balance or offset the external pressure that might otherwise cause the tank bottom to balloon. The API standard provides the equations necessary to calculate this minimum liquid level.[101]

The Petroleum Equipment Institute (PEI) publishes Recommended Practices (RP) for the petroleum industry. PEI RP-800, "Recommended Practices for Installation of Bulk Storage Plants," suggests anchoring tanks in flood plains and developing a plan to alleviate the accumulation of rainwater within a dike that can cause tanks to float.[102] PEI also states that aboveground storage tanks that are mounted in their own steel containment dikes should have the dike drainage valves opened during hurricanes, to allow potential flood waters to exit the diked area and thus help keep the tank from moving.

Wrapping and Protecting Pumps and Motors

Refinery and pipeline operations require many motors and pumps. Most are smaller pumps in the 200-hp range, but a number of very large pumps are also utilized. The smaller pumps weighing around 2,000 lb can be wrapped for protection or, if skid-mounted, lifted and relocated to higher elevation before the storm arrives. At least one company indicated that in 2008 they pulled motors off all key pumps at their facilities and wrapped them in plastic wrap to stop coils from getting wet.

Pipeline pump stations require multiple motors to provide the 10,000 hp required. Larger pumps exceeding 1,500 hp can weigh over 5,000 lb.[103] These units are too large to be wrapped or relocated. One pipeline operator explained their practice is to power down stations prior to a hurricane to prevent damage to motors and other equipment related to commercial power issues.

Facilitating Employee Evacuation and Reentry

Another priority for companies during storm preparation is to secure exemptions from evacuation orders so that restoration efforts can begin as soon as possible after a storm strikes. Companies work with Federal, State, and local governments to procure exemptions. At least one company reported working with local city mayors to secure exemptions from evacuations prior to hurricane landfall.

Companies have indicated that they use ride out crews, i.e., a small number of employees sheltering in place at storm-hardened facilities. The decision depends on facility location relative to storm path and the severity of the storm. Ride out crews assist in assessing damage and expediting restoration. At least two refiners indicated that they had built secure facilities to accommodate large crews.

Individual States may impose special evacuation standards. For example, Louisiana has developed a Standard Operating Procedure (SOP) for emergency response and management personnel at the State and local level in conjunction with critical infrastructure owners and operators.[104] Lack of uniform access guidelines after Hurricane Katrina resulted in delays and loss of critical utilities and services, as well as delays in reestablishing security and communications systems. The SOP protocol grants admission to the various facilities based on the immediate needs of the locally affected areas through communication with the local emergency operations center and parish and State Governments. The procedures are administered only in the event of a Declaration of a State of Emergency from the Governor or affected parish president or mayor when a mandatory evacuation order has been issued (see case study).

CASE STUDY: TIERED REENTRY APPROACH IN LOUISIANA

The procedure for allowing reentry into a secured area following an emergency evacuation in the State of Louisiana follows a tiered approach for reentry based on key roles in restoring normal operations after a disaster.

Tier 1	• Infrastructure and utilities repair personnel, including municipal and public works utilities requiring immediate access to restore water, lighting, and communications • Official Damage Assessment Teams including FEMA, State, and local officials • Other personnel at the discretion of the Parish DHS or applicable municipal EOC
Tier 2	• Relief workers to provide food and other supplies for people remaining in impacted areas • Healthcare agencies including hospitals, nursing homes, assisted living facilities, and dialysis centers • Insurance agents and banking organizations • Business operators considered critical to the recovery effort: transportation, public health, and rescue • Other personnel at the discretion of the Parish DHS or applicable municipal EOC
Tier 3	• Business operators not allowed in under Tier 2 and residents allowed to return as areas are deemed safe.

Note: Parish is the equivalent of a county in Louisiana. EOC is the emergency operations center.

Source: State of Louisiana, Standard Operating Procedure, Statewide Credentialing/ Access Program. http://www.lsp.org/pdf/lscap.pdf, accessed May 15, 2010.

In Texas, Chapter 22 of the Texas Labor Code prohibits an employer from discriminating against an employee who "leaves the employee's place of employment to participate in a general public evacuation ordered under an emergency evacuation order." However, Chapter 22 does not apply to a person who is necessary "to provide for the safety and well being of the general public, including a person necessary for the restoration of vital services." This is interpreted to include not only utility workers and other recovery personnel, but also employees working for gas stations, grocery stores and other critical services.[105]

After Hurricane Ike, one fuel supplier in Louisiana offered a bonus program incentive for people who stayed to help recovery efforts.[106]

Coordinating Priority Restoration and Waivers

Companies work with Federal, State, and local governments before a hurricane to secure waivers and permits that allow vital materials, including fuel and supplies, to be transported to affected areas as quickly as possible. Waivers cover the number of hours a truck driver can operate a vehicle, the weight of the truck bringing the fuel, and the quality of fuels. State and Federal regulations restrict the volatility of gasoline in summer months, and in certain urban areas reformulated gasoline may be required year-round. EPA may grant fuel quality waivers allowing early use of winter grade fuels, which normally enter the market in mid-September. EPA may also temporarily waive reformulated gasoline requirements. Additional waivers from State regulatory agencies may be necessary to receive additional fuel supplies from neighboring States.

PHMSA works with local and Federal agencies to assist with hurricane response and recovery efforts in several ways including:

- Facilitating the restoration of fuel distribution through pipelines to ensure sufficient levels of energy supplies
- Assisting in the design and implementation of emergency fuel distribution networks for FEMA
- Aiding in the ease of transfer and movement of hazardous materials throughout the hurricane-stricken region.

For example, during Hurricanes Katrina and Rita, PHMSA issued numerous Emergency Hazardous Materials Special Permits to Gulf Coast States authorizing the shipment and transportation of fuels that may not have fully complied with Hazardous Materials Regulations.[107]

The City of Gulfport has contracts in place with local service stations to provide priority access to fuel for city vehicles and equipment when the city is under emergency conditions. After Hurricane Katrina, access to gasoline and diesel fuel stored at these facilities was hampered by the lack of electric power for station pumps and manual pumps had to be employed.[108]

Several companies require employees to complete safety training before they transport any product. Drivers have to know the safety codes and requirements for each State they drive through. During hurricane events, companies use a wide pool of drivers. When drivers are trained and certified in advance, they can load their trucks without a delay during emergency situations. In Texas, the Fuel Team plays a pivotal role (see Case Study).

CASE STUDY: TEXAS FUEL TEAM IN PIVOTAL ROLE

After Hurricane Rita, Texas Governor Rick Perry created the Task Force on Evacuation, Transportation and Logistics. The Task Force recommended the creation of the Fuel Team to support the maintenance of fuel supplies along evacuation routes and to assist with recovery of the fuel network as quickly as possible after a storm. The Fuel Team was created to serve as a private-sector partner to the State and operates as an information clearinghouse and critical communications hub. Before the start of the hurricane season, the Fuel Team organizes and participates in State drills, and establishes communications procedures with refineries, retailers, pipelines, terminals and tankers. It proactively lays the groundwork necessary to obtain waivers for fuel, transportation, and re-entry for personnel and vehicles that are critical to recovery. During re-entry, the Fuel Team works with the Texas Department of Public Safety to plan for security, to arrange fuel carrier escorts, and to coordinate alternate routes for fuel deliveries. During Hurricane Ike, the Fuel Team worked directly with more than 40 State and Federal agencies, local jurisdictions, elected officials, and trade associations to support preparation, evacuation, search and rescue, and recovery.

Source: Texas Oil & Gas Association, *The Fuel Team Report*, November 11, 2008, http://www.txoga.org/categories/Resources/Downloads/, accessed June 26, 2010.

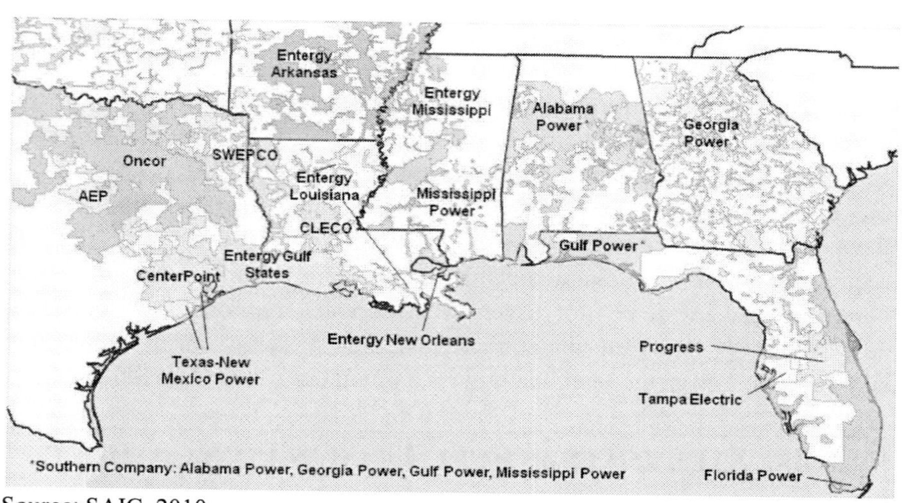

Source: SAIC, 2010.

Figure 15. Major Electric Utilities in the Gulf and Southeast.

Electricity Infrastructure

Electricity is an essential element of all energy supply and distribution systems and critical infrastructure (e.g., hospitals, banks, airports, transit systems). All segments of the energy supply and distribution infrastructure require electricity to operate. For example, a refinery or pipeline pumping station, even if undamaged by a hurricane, will not be able to operate if the supply of electricity to it is interrupted. This interdependence underscores the need for available grid-supplied electricity before, during, and after a hurricane.

The unprecedented hurricane seasons of 2004, 2005, and 2008 brought a renewed focus to the challenge of hardening the electric utility infrastructure, especially along the hurricane-prone Gulf Coast. Investor-owned utilities have shouldered significant expenditures in hardening and resiliency, not only because of the sheer number of residential and commercial customers served, but also because of their service to major refineries, pipeline and port terminals, and hurricane evacuation routes. Southern Company, as the parent of Alabama Power, Georgia Power, Gulf Power, and Mississippi Power, is the largest investor-owned utility in the region and provides service to a large number of customers in a wide geographic area. Entergy, with its Arkansas,

Gulf States, Louisiana, and New Orleans operating affiliates, is another strong presence in the region. A number of major investor-owned utilities also operate in Florida and Texas, however, and there are significant swaths of the region that are served by cooperatives and municipal utilities (pale yellow areas in Figure 15).

Because the United States enjoys considerable excess capacity in power generation, the loss of one or two large power plants does not necessarily black out thousands of customers or major petroleum facilities. The generation of power is also not the link in the electrical supply that is most vulnerable to storm damage. Rather, the electricity infrastructure most often damaged by hurricanes is the transmission and distribution (T&D) grid. Transmission lines deliver high voltage bulk electricity from the generation source to substations, where the voltage is stepped down for delivery along distribution lines to commercial and residential customers. Although storm-related outages do occur on transmission systems, about 90 percent of outages during a storm event occur along distribution systems.[109]

Impetus from Public Utility Commissions

Since 2005, State public utility commissions (PUCs) have issued rulemakings and/or regulatory activities related to storm hardening. Many of the T&D hardening and resiliency initiatives taken on by utilities have been in response to such regulation. The PUCs can also authorize inclusion of hardening and resiliency costs in the utilities' rate base. Specific initiatives include the following:

- Florida Public Service Commission (FPSC) initiated studies on the extent of the damage from the 2004-2005 hurricanes; introduced formal requirements for utilities to report annually on reliability and storm hardening; implemented a formal electric utility pole inspection program; funded university research on extreme wind damage; issued rulemakings; and published vegetation management best practices among storm hardening initiatives.[110]
- Louisiana Public Service Commission (LPSC) opened three dockets dealing with infrastructure hardening, undergrounding of existing overhead lines, and rate recovery from Hurricanes Gustav and Ike.[111]
- Public Utility Commission of Texas (PUCT) has issued at least eight rulemakings related to storm hardening – of which five remain open –

on central office emergency power and electric facilities in floodplains; reliability and continuity of service; infrastructure improvements; and maintenance reports.[112]

In their published material, these public utility commissions combine both hardening and resiliency activities under the single rubric of "storm hardening." This study differentiates storm hardening from infrastructure resiliency, as outlined in the *Definitions* section.

Electricity T&D Hardening

The first characteristic one should examine when considering storm hardening in the electricity sector is the increasing age of the T&D assets, which makes them more susceptible than newer assets to damage by hurricane winds and flooding. Another important consideration is that unlike downstream petroleum assets, which are discrete and limited in number, utility T&D assets are distributed throughout a wide geographic area.

To harden electricity infrastructure, utilities have made physical and structural improvements to lines, poles, towers, substations, and supporting facilities in order to make them less vulnerable to the damaging effects of hurricane winds and flooding, as well as to counteract the effects of an aging system. Specific hardening actions include:

- **Wind Protection**
  - **Upgrading damaged poles and structures**
  - **Strengthening poles with guy wires**
  - **Burying power lines underground**
- **Flood Protection**
  - **Elevating substations/control rooms**
  - **Relocating/constructing new lines and facilities**
- **Modernization**
  - **Installing asset tools and databases**
  - **Deploying sensors and control technology**

Wind Protection

Hurricane-force winds can cause extensive damage to electric utility T&D infrastructure, both directly and indirectly through damage to trees (see Table 5). In fact, wind damage poses a greater threat to electrical assets than flooding does. Storm surge and flooding can damage substations and control rooms whereas extreme winds can break and topple T&D poles and lines. Thousands of poles are widely dispersed to enable utilities to serve the region whereas only a few dozen substations and control rooms are located in flood-prone areas.

The Saffir-Simpson Hurricane Wind Scale is a 1 to 5 categorization based on a hurricane's intensity. The scale provides examples of the type of damage and impacts associated with winds of the indicated intensity. In general, damage rises by about a factor of four for every category increase.[113]

As shown in the table, hurricane-force winds can bend and topple T&D poles and structures. When poles are bent but still in working order, linemen will generally straighten rather than replace the poles. Following a hurricane, many more poles are usually straightened than replaced. Damaged poles may be replaced with wood or upgraded to stronger materials. Utility poles on Galveston demonstrated the value of alternative materials during Hurricane Ike when none of the concrete poles were downed but all the wood poles on a bridge between islands were broken.[114]

Table 5. Saffir-Simpson Hurricane Winds and Selected Impacts

Category	Winds	Impact to Trees	Impacts to Power Lines
1	74-95 mph	Large branches of trees will snap and shallow rooted trees can be toppled.	Extensive damage to power lines and poles will likely result in power outages that could last a few to several days.
2	96-110 mph	Many shallowly rooted trees will be snapped or uprooted and block numerous roads.	Near-total power loss is expected with outages that could last from several days to weeks.
3	111-130 mph	Many trees will be snapped or uprooted, blocking numerous roads.	Electricity will be unavailable for several days to a few weeks after the storm passes.
4	131-155 mph	Most trees will be snapped or uprooted and power poles downed.	Power outages will last for weeks to possibly months.
5	> 155 mph	Nearly all trees will be snapped or uprooted and power poles downed.	Power outages will last for weeks to possibly months.

Source: NOAA, National Weather Service, National Hurricane Center, http://www.nhc.noaa.gov/pdf/sshws_table.pdf, accessed May 22, 2010.

Upgrading Damaged Poles and Structures

The most common hardening practice for electric T&D systems is upgrading poles and structures with stronger materials. All of the utilities interviewed for this study identified pole upgrades as their primary hardening strategy. For distribution systems, this usually involves upgrading wooden poles to concrete, steel, or a composite material, and installing guys and other structural supports. Transmission structures are typically upgraded from aluminum to galvanized steel lattice or concrete.

Materials are typically upgraded to meet certain grade and wind loading criteria as defined by IEEE's National Electrical Safety Code (NESC).[115] The NESC contains a set of standards that provides consistency and safety to the design, construction, and operation of electric supply lines and associated equipment. The NESC specifies three grades for pole material strength: Grades B, C, and N, of which B is the highest (see Table 6). As written, the NESC standards are voluntary; however, some PUCs require utilities under their jurisdiction to adhere to specific standards when upgrading utility poles.

The NESC also defines extreme wind loading criteria applicable to structures higher than 60 feet, based on a map of local wind loads (see Figure 16). There is no consistent wind loading applied universally. For the Gulf Coast region, wind loads range from 120 mph inland to 150 mph near the coast. Some utilities have independently chosen to upgrade to specific NESC wind loading standards. For example, Entergy Louisiana requires that all new transmission lines be able to withstand 150 mph wind in the coastal tip of the State and 140 mph further inland.[116]

Table 6. NESC Utility Pole Grades

Grade	Description
B	More conservative installation with higher safety factors and lower potential load applied to the structure. Highest grade typically corresponds to crossings (highway and railroad) and lines carrying variable voltage levels.
C	Less conservative installation with a lower safety factor and higher potential load applied to the structure. Lower than Grade B and typical for power or joint telecommunications/power distribution pole applications.
N	Lowest grade of construction; typically used in telecommunication applications.

Source: Institute of Electrical and Electronics Engineers (IEEE), National Electrical Safety Codes (NESC), August 2006, http://standards.ieee.org/nesc/, accessed May 22, 2010.

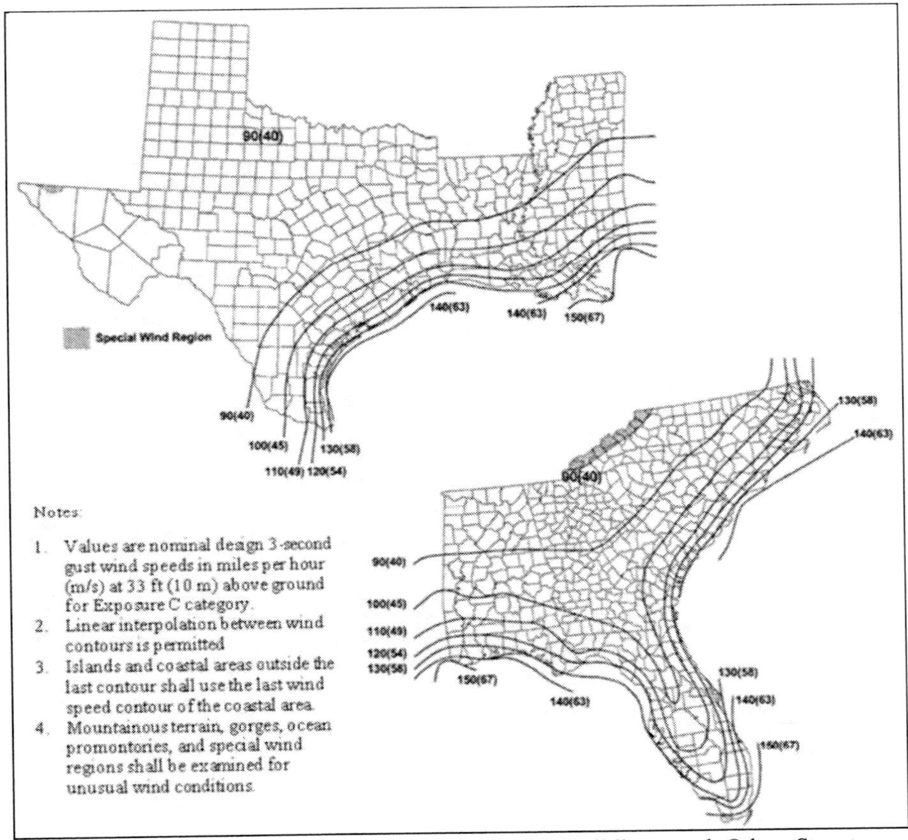

Source: ASCE 7-05, Minimum Design Loads for Buildings and Other Structures, ASCE Publications, Reston, VA, 2005.

Figure 16. Extreme Wind Loading on the U.S. Southeast Coastline.

The PUCT has recommended that all new and replacement transmission structures installed within ten miles of the Texas coastline be designed to meet the current NESC wind loading standards, assuming a maximum wind speed of 140 mph. The Commission is considering extending this standard to all permanent new and replacement structures installed within 50 miles of the Texas coastline.[117]

The FPSC requires that all new and replacement poles be constructed to Grade B requirements. In 2008 alone, compliance with this requirement affected the replacement of thousands of T&D poles (see Table 7).[118]

Table 7. Florida Utility Compliance with NESC Criteria in 2008

Utility	Replaced	With
Florida Power & Light	18,000 distribution poles	steel or concrete poles
Progress Energy	866 distribution poles	steel or concrete poles
	1,096 transmission poles	
Tampa Electric	650 structure replacements	steel or concrete poles
	139 sets of insulators	polymer insulators

Sources: Florida Power & Light, Progress Energy, and Tampa Electric Progress Distribution Reliability Reports 2008, http://www.psc.state.fl.us/utilities/electricgas/docs/2008DistributionReliabilityReport.pdf, accessed June 10, 2010.

Such efforts require significant investment. Tampa Electric's 2008 pole upgrades, for example were budgeted at $12.3 million. For 2009, Tampa Electric budgeted $10.7 million to replace 584 structures with steel or concrete poles, and 99 sets of insulators with polymer replacements.[119]

Strengthening Poles with Guy Wires

Strengthening poles and towers by installing guy wires and upgrading crossarm materials is another common hardening method. Adding guy wires can increase the strength of a pole without the need for full pole replacement (see Figure 17). Upgrading crossarm material allows for the strengthening of a structure with minimal material replacement.

There are no specific standards outlined for guying poles. Industry practices are:

- Transmission towers: a minimum of two to four anchors/guys
- Distribution poles: two anchors

T&D poles subject to storm surges and flooding require guying. Costs and procedures for installing guy wires vary according to the height of the pole or structure, soil characteristics, assembly configuration, and design wind speed. For example, if lines pass through marshes, it may be necessary to dig as much as 100 feet deep to install anchors for the guy wires, substantially increasing cost. The most expensive guying involves pole installation in sand and silt soils.

Company interviews revealed typical guying costs of $600 and $1,900 per pole. Guying for extreme winds can as much as double those costs to $1,500 – $3,100 per pole.

Source: OSHA. http://www.osha.gov/SLTC/etools/electri c_power/images/distribution _system_line s.jpg. Accessed May 14, 2010.

Figure 17. Distribution Pole with Guy Wires.

Gulf Power's two priority hardening activities in 2008 included installing guys on H-frame structures and replacing wooden cross arms with steel cross arms on transmission structures. Over 300 Gulf Power structures were hardened in 2008 at a cost of $600,000.[120] The Florida Public Utilities Company requires storm guys or bracing for additional support on lines that are located near the coast or inland waterways and are subject to storm surges or flooding.[121]

Burying Power Lines Underground

Placing utility lines underground eliminates their susceptibility to lightning and wind damage. Underground utility lines present significant challenges, however, including additional repair time and much higher installation and repair costs (see case study, below). Investor-owned utilities in North Carolina compared five years of underground and overhead reliability data, and found that the frequency of outages on underground systems was 50% less than for overhead systems, but the average duration of an underground outage was 58% longer.[122]

Perhaps the most important issue for coastal regions is that underground wires are more susceptible to damage from storm surge flooding than overhead wires. For example, frequent and prolonged flooding in 2004 and 2005 resulted in water intrusion and corrosion to Progress Energy's underground equipment in Florida.[123]

Source: Gulf Power Company, Electric Infrastructure Workshop, January 23, 2006 presentation, http://www.floridapsc.com/utilities/electricgas/EIProject/docs/GulfPower.ppt, accessed June 10, 2010.

Figure 18. Underwater Cable Crossing Exposed.

Gulf Power reported in 2005 that some of its underground assets in coastal communities were washed out to sea (see Figure 18). On the Alabama coast, Hurricane Ivan's storm surge and wave action physically uncovered and destroyed miles of underground lines in 2004, and as a result, some locations remained without power for more than a year.[124]

There is no precise cost per mile for undergrounding wires; every construction project is unique because load, number of customers served, and construction parameters can vary widely. There are hidden costs, (e.g., customer meter conversions, coolants and pumping stations). However, company interviews indicate that burying overhead wires costs between $500,000 and $2 million per mile, plus expenses for coolants and pumping stations. One Texas utility, Southwestern Electric Power Company, estimated a 79% premium for undergrounding, with the cost of overhead wires at $250,000 per circuit mile and undergrounding at $447,200 per circuit mile.[125]

Flood Protection

Storm surge exerts pressure on everything in its path and causes soil erosion, especially around solid objects. In coastal areas, breaking waves carry floating debris that can cause extensive physical damage. With such destructive characteristics, storm surge presents many hazards to utility T&D networks.

Unlike petroleum facilities, distributed utility T&D assets are not usually protected by berms or levees. It is far less expensive to replace damaged or destroyed substations and control rooms than to build and maintain flood protection around each one. Facility replacement sometimes involves rebuilding at an elevation above the storm surge levels or relocation to an area less subject to flooding.

CASE STUDY: LOUISIANA UTILITIES UNLIKELY TO BURY POWER LINES

The drawbacks and costs of undergrounding power lines exceeded the benefits for Louisiana utilities susceptible to tidal surges and flooding.

Benefits	• Lower right-of-way maintenance (vegetation management) costs • Better visual aesthetics • Better reliability during severe weather (high winds, lightning) • Fewer momentary interruptions • Reduced storm damage from broken poles, downed lines, airborne debris • Reduced accidents from vehicles hitting poles
Drawbacks	• Traffic disruption from installation trenching and/or boring under roads • Need for oil or gas coolants to insulate cables and circulating pumping stations • Need for burying co-located utilities (cable TV, telephone, Internet) • Longer duration of outages than for overhead lines • Greater susceptibility to tidal surges, flooding, and saltwater contamination • Greater susceptibility to damage during recovery for pad-mounted transformers • Greater susceptibility to outages from digging for equipment and cables • More complicated inspections • Lower system-life expectancy • Costs to customer for meter conversion • Overhead system becomes stranded asset
Costs	• 5-10 times the cost of overhead lines for larger distribution lines • $0.5-2.0 million per mile installed, plus coolants and pumping stations • $1,500-4,500 per customer conversion

Source: LPSC Docket Search Page. Docket No. R-30821. https://p8.lpsc.org/Workplace/Search.jsp, accessed June 10, 2010.

Elevating Substations and Control Rooms

Substations are an integral part of the utility distribution system. They are the hubs where electricity from high-voltage transmission lines is stepped down to a voltage suitable for commercial and residential use. They also serve to isolate faults in the distribution system and provide voltage regulation.[126] The most prevalent cause of damage to substations in coastal regions is flooding from storm surge.

During Hurricanes Katrina and Rita, low-lying power substations in Mississippi and Louisiana suffered significant damage to controllers, switches, and other components due to storm surge and waves (see Figure 19). A NIST report determined that even equipment that was pressure washed with fresh water immediately after the storm would have to be replaced because saltwater flooding promoted rapid corrosion of internal electrical components.[127]

One common hardening practice that utilities reported using to protect against storm surge is elevating substations. As part of Southwest Louisiana Electric Membership Corporation's hardening plan, for example, three substations that were flooded by Hurricanes Rita and Ike were elevated above the storm surge plus five feet, for a total of 13 feet above sea level (see Figure 20). The cost of elevating the three substations was estimated at $5.2 million.[128]

Some State commissions have recommended construction guidelines for substations. For example, the PUCT recommends that all electric utilities located within a 100-year floodplain anywhere in the State design and construct all new substations so that the floor of the control house and all water-sensitive components and operating equipment are above the elevation of that 100-year floodplain.[129]

In order to determine how high to elevate substations, control rooms, and other critical assets, utilities often use the Seas and Lakes Overland Surges (SLOSH) model developed by NOAA/NHC. SLOSH is a computerized model that estimates storm surge heights and winds resulting from historical, hypothetical, or predicted hurricanes.[130]

A number of substations along the Gulf Coast have been elevated 25 feet based on SLOSH predictions for Category 3 hurricanes. Because Category 4 and 5 hurricanes are relatively rare, the costs of elevating coastal substations to withstand those events often outweigh the potential benefits. For that reason, a number of utilities have decided not to elevate substations to that level, opting instead to invest in spare equipment to address that risk. In cases where elevating is not feasible, a few utilities have installed cement walls or earthen levees to protect from flooding. Other utilities have required that new substations be constructed in areas that are not located in flood zones.

Relocating and Constructing Lines and Facilities

Emergency operations centers, distribution or energy delivery operations centers, and communications and IT facilities are critical components of any electrical supply system, and utilities have taken measures to harden these resources. In some cases, utilities have relocated critical facilities away from flood-prone areas. Other hardening practices include strengthening the existing buildings that contain vulnerable equipment and moving equipment to upper floors where it will not be damaged in the event of a flood. Utilities have also mounted re-closers, capacitors, or regulators that require electronic controls above maximum anticipated surge or flood levels along T&D lines.[131]

Hurricane Katrina destroyed 120,000 square feet of Southern Company office space near Gulfport, Mississippi, including the storm center located at Plant Watson. Southern redesigned, rebuilt, and constructed its new Corporate Storm Center in a secure location 10 miles inland and at a higher elevation above sea level. The facility has the capability to withstand 200 mph winds and has its own backup generation system and additional workstations. It also features state-of- the-art electronics to enhance the ability to track storms, facilitate system restoration efforts, and improve communications both internally and externally.[132]

Source: NIST, Performance *of Physical Structures in Hurricane Katrina and Hurricane Rita: A Reconnaissance Report,* www.bfrl.nist.gov/investigations/pubs/NIST_TN_1476.pdf, accessed June 26, 2010.

Figure 19. Substation Damage in Vermilion Parish, Louisiana.

Source: *SLEMCO Power* Jan-Feb 2010, "SLEMCO Engineers a New Approach to Protect ERATH's Substation," www.slemco.com/pdf_folder/magpdfs110/JF10PG7. PdF, accessed June 26, 2010.

Figure 20. Elevated Substation in Vermilion Parish, Louisiana.

Hurricane Katrina also flooded Southern's Alabama Power distribution Operations Center in Mobile, Alabama. The Emergency Operations Center was on the fourth floor, but the 12-foot surge that flooded the building knocked out the backup generator and activated the fire alarm, causing staff evacuation. Southern decided to construct a new state-of-the-art distribution Operations Center in West Mobile, 15 miles inland and 202 feet above sea level. The new 11,000-square-foot building is constructed of concrete blocks, has a roof able to withstand Category 3 winds, and is self-sufficient.[133]

Entergy was required to move its energy delivery operations to Clinton, Mississippi after its headquarters in New Orleans were flooded during Hurricane Katrina. Entergy decided to consolidate its operational structure in Jackson, Mississippi where the company constructed a new Operations Complex for more than $25 million. The new facility incorporates Entergy's storm response command center, transmission, and nuclear business, and was completed in 2009.[134] Also in 2009, Entergy completed a program to install automatic failover capabilities at its control centers. With this new feature, if a hurricane takes a control center out of service, functions will transfer to another control center so that all operating data are recovered quickly.[135]

Modernization

The electricity T&D system is aging and investment in new construction was declining for decades. Construction of new electric transmission facilities decreased by about 30 percent between 1975 and 2000 as annual investment in new transmission facilities declined.[136] In addition, many utilities have transformer assets that are 40 to 50 years old, which is an age at which failures begin to increase rapidly.[137]

After 2000, the trend reversed and investment in transmission infrastructure began increasing in response to reliability and generator interconnection requirements, and several landmark developments in Federal and State policies (e.g., Energy Policy Act of 2005, State renewable portfolio standards, Federal transmission pricing policy, and Federal initiatives promoting transmission Smart Grid development under the American Recovery and Reinvestment Act). From 2001 to 2008, Edison Electric Institute members invested nearly $57.5 billion in transmission infrastructure improvements. The Southern Company, Oncor, and Progress have invested $4 billion, $2.5 billion, and $1.6 billion, respectively over the same period. Their collective investment represents 14 percent of the total identified. In fact, the Southern Company reported the second largest investment of all companies surveyed.[138]

Utilities in the Southeast and Gulf Coast are investing in new technologies aimed at modernizing their T&D grid, such as improved SCADA systems, Phasor Measurement Units, and advanced switching mechanisms to self-diagnose and repair problems and promote greater efficiency of the grid.

Installing Asset Tools and Databases

Electric utilities rely on complex IT and communications systems to monitor and control their T&D grid. These systems operate continuously and play a key role in hurricane response and recovery by enabling utility controllers to identify damaged assets and dispatch repair crews quickly and efficiently. Technologies include SCADA systems, substation automation, automated mapping and facilities management, and geographic information systems (GIS).

SCADA systems consist of computer networks that are used to control and monitor power grids, using remote terminal units (RTUs) to collect data from geographically dispersed equipment such as transformers and substations. The RTUs employ a variety of communications technologies to transfer information from the remote location to a control center, including wired networks, wireless cellular networks, Internet communications, microwaves, fiber optic cable, and satellite. Several utilities have even installed private telephone systems with high-speed switching and automatic fault recovery capabilities.[139] Equipment in the field can then be controlled remotely. Traditional SCADA systems (that could control substations and selected distribution automation devices) were early Smart Grid technologies. Advances in SCADA technology are one of the key components in the effort to create a Smart Grid in the United States.[140]

Substation automation uses computer-based control and monitoring technology to create highly reliable, self-healing power systems that can rapidly respond to real-time events.[141] They can work in combination with SCADA systems or independently. Recent developments in communication technologies have enabled cost-effective remote-control systems which have the capability of monitoring the real-time operating conditions and performances of substations. Many systems use hybrid communications networks that include Internet and wireless networks to reduce cost and increase reliability for substation automation applications.

Automated Mapping and Facilities Management (AM/FM) involves the use of Computer Aided design (CAD) and GIS software to automate the mapping of assets and facilities and aid in the management of those facilities. A key advantage of this technology is the ability to share maps easily between utilities and Federal and State agencies.[142] After Hurricane Rita, Entergy Texas upgraded the AM/FM system used in its distribution Operations Center in Beaumont. The system now provides instant information regarding the status of equipment throughout Southeast Texas. Upgrades included improvements to the system used to dispatch workers when outages occur.[143]

As Hurricane Ike approached the Texas coast, CenterPoint Energy used GIS-based damage prediction models to approximate how many customers would lose power, what the infrastructure damage would be, and how quickly repairs could be made. They placed supply orders based on predicted damages so crews would be fully stocked and ready to make repairs once the storm subsided. Since the damage model warned that Galveston Island would soon be under water, CenterPoint pulled supplies from the area and relocated crews. After the storm, they used GIS to create maps of damaged areas and share the information with customers, media, government, and support agencies.[144]

Deploying Sensors and Control Technology

New or upgraded technologies can harden transmission monitoring and control systems. The North American SynchroPhasor Initiative (NASPI) – a consortium of DOE/OE, the North American Electric Reliability Corporation

(NERC), national laboratories, and utilities – is working to advance the deployment and use of networked synchrophasors or Phasor Measurement Units (PMUs) and the sharing of their data.[145] PMUs are remote real-time sensing devices that measure voltage, current, and frequency on an electricity grid to determine the health of the system. They are used in conjunction with SCADA systems and provide a number of advantages. PMUs include GIS devices that are time-synchronized with frequency measurements of up to 30 samples per second, providing real-time, geographically relevant information. The typical SCADA system has a sampling rate of once every few seconds, and is not usually GIS-enabled.

The installation of intelligent control devices such as PMUs can help keep systems in balance during times of system problems, damage, and interruptions. Investments in automated metering, Smart Grid, and "intelligent grid" technologies can help companies quickly detect and isolate specific areas of trouble. As a result, utilities are taking existing devices, such as disturbance fault recorders and relays that have PMU functionality, and converting those to act as PMUs. NASPI members have prepared resources that explain how to convert devices, how to install a new PMU, and how to interconnect the devices. PMUs can provide improved system restoration and event analysis during a major disturbance such as a hurricane. The following case study addresses Entergy's deployment of state-of-the-art sensors developed with OE funding.

Case Study: Entergy Keeps Lights on with PMUs

During Hurricane Gustav in 2008, Entergy had 14 transmission lines out, a condition that created a Baton Rouge-New Orleans electrical island for 33 hours (i.e., interconnection to the utility grid was lost). During this period, Entergy was able to control the island's frequency, balance three large generating units, and maintain electric service to customers because of the 21 PMUs the company had installed across a four-state area. PMUs identified and warned of islanding conditions during emergencies and provided Entergy with insight into how to manage islands and where else in the territory additional PMUs were needed. Entergy was unique in that no other hurricane-impacted utility had experimented with PMUs. Entergy's success with PMUs during Gustav is viewed as replicable with other utilities in storm paths.

Source: DOE/OE, Transmission Reliability - More Information, http://www.oe.energy.gov/transmission_02.htm. Accessed May 7, 2010.

Electricity T&D Resiliency

Improving the resiliency of electricity infrastructure involves preparing T&D systems to continue operating despite damage. Resiliency efforts also involve increasing a system's ability to return to normal operations rapidly if outages do occur. Resiliency measures may be general, taking the form of best practices that apply to any hurricane, or they may be special measures taken to prepare for a specific storm.

General Readiness

General readiness activities may occur before hurricane season or throughout the year. For example, Gulf Coast and Southeast utilities perform annual updates to their hurricane preparedness plans and train staff throughout the year. They follow standard cycles for inspecting T&D poles and structures, for managing vegetation along rights-of-way, and for participating in a number of mutual assistance groups. In addition, utilities that provide linemen and tree trimmers to other utilities during emergencies will receive comparable assistance when they need it.

Some general readiness efforts are regulated by PUCs and other State agencies. Florida and Texas PUCs have required utilities to document their readiness activities (see Table 8). The PUCT issued its rulemaking on June 23, 2010 requiring all Texas utilities to update storm hardening plans every five years and address distribution pole inspection and replacement.[146]

This section addresses the general readiness efforts utilities undertake:

- **Conducting hurricane preparedness planning and training**
- **Complying with inspection protocols**
- **Managing vegetation**
- **Participating in mutual assistance groups**
- **Purchasing or leasing mobile transformers and substations**
- **Procuring spare T&D equipment**

Table 8. Year-Round Readiness Efforts

Planning & Training	Update Emergency Operations Plan (EOP) regularly
	Create a web-based EOP and roster for aligning skills during restoration
	Enhance EOP training and drills
	Update all information templates for storm restoration reporting
	Train non-field personnel to handle logistics and customers
Inspecting Poles	Implement distribution wood pole inspection program (with visual, sound/bore, or excavation audits at regular intervals)
	Conduct inspections on all transmission line poles • Aerial patrol of system at least four times per year • Walking, ground, and detailed climbing inspections at least once every six years
Managing Vegetation	Perform vegetation management activities in multi-year cycles • Main feeders every three years • Laterals every six years • Danger trees as soon as possible
	Place facilities on public rights-of-way to secure private easements
Mutual Aid & Logistics	Develop central database to manage/track logistic support, mutual aid crews
	Request self-sufficient mutual aid crews
	Computerize check-in/out procedures for restoration crews
	Identify new staging areas and pre-stage logistics before hurricane landfall
	Work with cities and counties to convey accurate information and improve public perception

Sources: Adapted from CenterPoint: submitted 1/17/2006, http://interchange.puc.state.tx.us/WebApp/Interchange/Documents/32182_7_500961.PDF, TXU: submitted 1/17/2006, http://interchange.puc.state.tx.us/WebApp/Interchange/Documents/32182_11_501083.PDF, AEP: submitted 1/17/2006, http://interchange.puc.state.tx.us/WebApp/Interchange/Documents/32182_12_501105.PDF, Entergy: submitted 1/17/2006, http://interchange.puc.state.tx.us/WebApp/Interchange/Documents/32182_13_501108.PDF, FPUC Distribution Reliability Report 2008. http://www.psc.state.fl.us/utilities/electricgas/docs/2008DistributionReliabilityReport.pdf, Florida PSC, Report to the Legislature on Enhancing the Reliability of Florida's Distribution and Transmission Grids During Extreme Weather (Update to July 2007 Report), July 2008, http://www.floridapsc.com/utilities/electricgas/eiproject/docs/AddendumSHLegislature.pdf, Florida PSC, Order No. PSC-06-0351-PAA-EI, April 25, 2006. http://www.psc.state.fl.us/library/filings/06%5C03645-06%5C03645-06.PDF, accessed December 2009.

Conducting Hurricane Preparedness Planning and Training

All utilities located in the Gulf Coast and Southeast perform annual reviews of their hurricane preparedness plans, incorporating lessons learned from the prior year. In tabletop exercises and simulations, personnel are trained to respond effectively. These exercises are normally scheduled in May, preceding hurricane season (see case study).

CASE STUDY: FPL SIMULATES PLANNING AND RESPONSE TO VIRTUAL HURRICANE

Employees from across the company recently participated in the annual hurricane drill to practice Florida Power & Light's emergency response plan, which includes tracking outages, assessing damage, communicating with customers and employees, and initiating service restoration. Throughout the simulation, FPL tested its storm plans and tactics, applying lessons learned from previous hurricanes and other extreme weather events.

Source: "FPL Simulates Planning and Response to Virtual Hurricane Ari in Preparation for 2010 Storm Season," *Wall Street Journal*, http://www.marketwatch.com/story/fpl-simulates-planning-and-response-to-virtual-hurricane-ari-in-preparation-for-2010-storm-season-2010-05-07?reflink=MW_news_stmp, accessed May 10, 2010.

Complying with Inspection Protocols

Inspecting distribution poles and transmission structures are the most common resiliency activities. They are performed both year round and in preparation for particular storms. Pole inspections are a type of preventative maintenance. They maximize T&D asset life, gather the information necessary to manage and prioritize asset needs and resources, and minimize unscheduled or emergency maintenance of poles or the lines they support.

Wooden distribution poles are visually inspected for rot, ground line decay, and insect or woodpecker damage. If there are no visual signs of pole decomposition, then the pole may be sounded and bored. Sounding the pole involves knocking the pole with a hammer while listening and feeling for less obvious defects such as above ground voids caused by decay, loose shell, or overhead hardware that has loosened (see Figure 21). Boring uses a bit or increment borer to probe areas identified as suspect through sounding and visual inspection.

Transmission lines can be inspected visually, from vehicle or aircraft, or by climbing the structures. Some State PUCs have instituted mandatory inspection cycles for transmission circuits. FPSC requires each investor-owned utility to inspect their entire transmission system on a six-year cycle.[147]

CenterPoint Energy instituted a proactive five-year inspection and maintenance cycle for all transmission circuits, a ten-year wood pole treatment cycle, and a galvanized steel painting program to prevent corrosion on steel structures.[148]

Utilities are increasingly using infrared technology to scan and identify problems with transmission lines and other electrical equipment. When components of electrical systems begin to fail, a common symptom is a significant temperature difference between ailing components and their surroundings. Infrared scanning equipment mounted on vehicles or aircraft can detect and record anomalies so they can be repaired before failure.[149]

Managing Vegetation

The most effective storm-resiliency activity is widening transmission line rights-of-way. Even if a structure is designed to withstand high wind speeds, it will not resist the impact force of a 3-ton tree flying at 120 mph.[150] Tree- and vegetation-related damage to power lines is the most common cause of electricity outages.[151] Utility Vegetation Management Plans involve the clearing of potentially damaging tree limbs and other vegetation from power line rights-of-way. Although tree-related damage is more common for distribution lines, tree-related transmission outages are also a regular event.

Source: Pole Maintenance Company, Pole Inspection Method, http://www.pmcpole.com/documents/inspection/methods.aspx, accessed April 12, 2010.

Figure 21. Wood Pole Being Sounded.

In 2006, NERC introduced the Transmission Vegetation Management Program, also known as NERC Standard FAC-003-1. This standard aims to prevent tree-related outages by requiring transmission owners to control vegetation growth in and around transmission rights-of-way, and to report vegetation-related outages to their respective regional reliability organizations and to NERC.[152] Transmission lines operated at 200kV or more are covered, as well as any lines of a lower voltage that have been designated by the utilities as critical to the regional electrical system. According to the standard, transmission owners must prepare and maintain a formal transmission vegetation management program that identifies and documents the clearances between supply lines and surrounding vegetation, taking into consideration factors such as voltage, temperature, and wind. The program must also define a schedule for routine vegetation inspections and abatement.

Under the reporting requirements of NERC Standard FAC-003-1, tree-related outages are categorized by cause and are penalized accordingly:

- Category 1 outages are those caused by vegetation growing into lines from either inside or outside the right-of-way.
- Category 2 outages are those caused by vegetation falling onto lines from within the right-of- way.
- Category 3 outages are those caused by vegetation falling onto lines from outside the right- of-way.

Because Category 1 and 2 outages are preventable, they are considered to be violations of NERC Standard FAC-003-1. Category 3 outages are not considered to be violations of the standard.

In addition to adhering to NERC standards for transmission lines, electric utility companies work year round to prevent tree-related damage to distribution lines, with special attention paid to vulnerable corridors in the event of an approaching storm. FPSC requires all utilities to perform vegetation management on a three-year cycle for all distribution systems.[153] For example, Florida Public Utilities Company practices a vegetation management plan that includes trimming around main feeders every three years, around smaller circuits every six years, and addressing specific tree hazards as soon as possible.[154]

Participating in Mutual Assistance Groups

The damage from a major hurricane is often too much for one utility to manage on its own. For this reason, electric utilities have banded together to form mutual assistance groups through which they work together to plan a coordinated response to electrical outages. In the face of a storm or other emergency, personnel from unaffected areas mobilize immediately to assist in the restoration effort of the affected area. With proper planning, the safety and communications issues associated with the restoration effort, including guidelines and contingencies, have been worked out before the onset of the emergency. Furthermore, these recovery plans often allow for a decentralized chain of command, so that decisions can be made quickly by the authority with the greatest situational awareness.

There are nine regional mutual assistance groups (RMAGs) in the United States (see Figure 22).[155] RMAGs provide a forum to ensure safe, effective, and coordinated restoration efforts, and establish additional guidelines that aid in the communication process, rapid mobilization and response by qualified personnel, and minimize misunderstanding before, during, and after the assistance is sent. Assistance is not, however, limited by regional borders. Through the coordination of the Edison Electrical Institute, utilities often assist in the restoration efforts of other regions.

Emergency planners for Mississippi Power assumed a direct hit three days before Hurricane Katrina made landfall. They began making requests for personnel to aid in the restoration. Because of existing damage in Florida, however, and because the storm threatened the entire northern Gulf Coast, there was a shortage of available linemen in the region. With the help of RMAGs, however, 2,400 outside workers were in place and ready to begin work before the storm had passed. Within seven days of the storm, 10,800 workers from 23 States and Canada were assisting with the restoration effort.[156]

Days before Hurricane Ike made landfall, CenterPoint Energy made a similar request for the help of mutual assistance crews. After the storm, about 12,000 line mechanics, tree-trimmers, and other personnel arrived in Houston, representing more than 70 companies from 30 States and Canada. Participation in mutual assistance more than quadrupled the CenterPoint corps of 3,300 restoration workers.[157]

A growing concern among mutual assistance planners is the need for outside work crews to arrive in an affected area with the supplies they need to be self-sufficient. The costs and logistics of a restoration effort can be staggering. Work crews must be provided not only with the equipment and materials they need to make repairs, but also with food, shelter, security, and sanitation. depending on the size and nature of the disaster, it may become difficult, if not impossible, for the local utility to provide the basic necessities to its mutual assistance partners. One company indicated that RMAG crews now plan to arrive in disaster areas fully equipped for self-sufficiency.

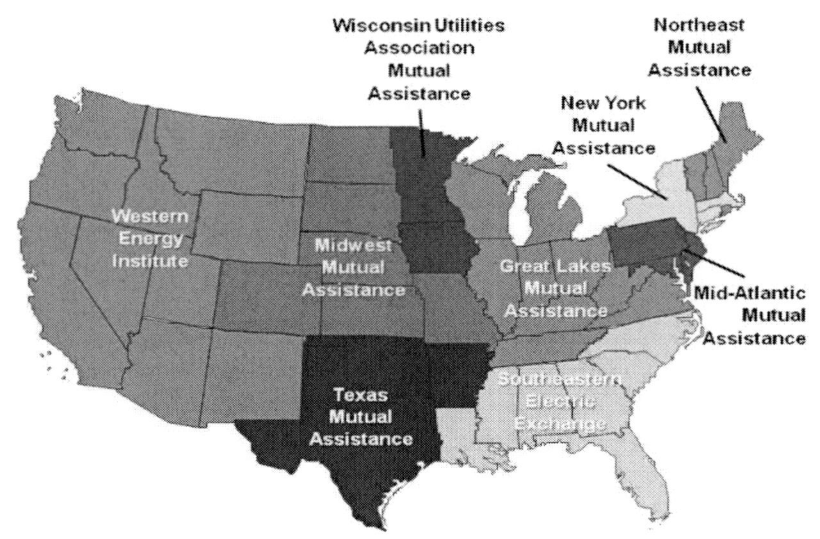

Note: This map is representational as most utilities belong to multiple RMAGs.
Source: Adapted from AEP, http://winupoh.org/events/event_details/2009/3-27%20Nowak%20Presentation.pdf, accessed June 14, 2010.

Figure 22. Regional Mutual Assistance Groups.

Purchasing or Leasing Mobile Transformers and Substations

Mobile transformers and substations can be used by utilities to temporarily replace substation transformers in the low and medium power range (10- 100 MVA) that are damaged by a hurricane. Mobile substations include the trailer, switchgear, breakers, emergency or station power supply, a compact high-power-density transformer, and enhanced cooling capability (see Figure 23). They enable the temporary restoration of grid service by circumventing damaged substation equipment, allowing time for repairs. Mobile transformers can be operational and restore the flow of electricity in some cases within 12-24 hours.

Mobile transformer systems are too small to replace high-power transformers (> 100 MVA) and are not suitable for specialized facilities that require guaranteed electric service to function. Where disruption is prolonged due to equipment failure or total destruction, however, mobile substations and transformers can play a critical role in reestablishing grid connection.[158]

In preparation for a hurricane, mobile substations are placed in strategic locations near at-risk substations, but far enough to avoid the same risks. This helps to reduce the time necessary for deployment should a substation incur damage. Utilities reported having several mobile substations in different voltages and sizes.

Procuring Spare T&D Equipment

As noted earlier, the costs of certain hardening activities – such as elevating substations or undergrounding power lines – can sometimes outweigh the benefits. In addition to cost, practical considerations may also preclude the use of a given hardening technique. day-to-day operations at a substation, for example, are much more difficult when the entire apparatus is raised 25 feet off the ground. For situations like these, utilities can mitigate risk by arranging in advance for spare equipment and materials, so that they are prepared to make rapid repairs when a hurricane does hit.

As a resiliency measure, the procurement of spare equipment does not require utilities to rely entirely on a cache of unused transformers, poles, and conductors. Many utilities have agreements in place with manufacturers and suppliers of needed materials. In such "strategic sourcing agreements" vendors may offer favorable pricing, performance measures, and volume, as well as guaranteed lead times, in return for the privilege of being the utility's primary or exclusive supplier of a particular material. For example, in Texas, Oncor Electric delivery has arrangements with Hubbell and S&C Electric Company for the delivery of emergency supplies, some of which have been delivered overnight. Oncor also has an equipment agreement with ABB/Power Partners, a vendor of single-phase pole-mounted transformers. Under this agreement, the utility stores the spare transformers in its own facilities, but does not pay for them until they need to be installed.[159]

During hurricane season, CenterPoint Energy keeps enough spare poles, spools of wire, transformers, and other hardware on hand to keep repair crews supplied until orders from the manufacturers can be delivered. The utility has arrangements with Thomas & Betts for transmission structures, Southwire for conductor, Central Maloney for distribution transformers, and Thomasson Lumber Co. for wood poles. On September 11, 2008, two days before Hurricane Ike even made landfall, Southwire's first truckload of wire left the plant. Southwire has reported that to meet demand, it continued to ship cable every day until the end of September. during that post-Ike recovery period, Southwire shipped almost nine million feet (over 1,700 miles) of cable.[160]

Redundant communications systems are also essential to ensuring continuity of operations in the event that telecommunications utilities are off-line or power is lost after a storm. Some utilities have expanded satellite communications capabilities with mobile satellite trailers that can be deployed to field staging areas and include full capabilities for email, internet, outage management systems, VOIP telephones, and portable and fixed satellite phones. Others have redundant fiber optics. Southern Company has its own dedicated communications system, SouthernLINC, built specifically to its own specifications. Some PUCs have designated specific telecommunications standards in their States. For example, PUCT has recommended that all Texas telecommunications utilities' central offices in hurricane-prone areas should be capable of full operation without interruption for at least 72 hours after loss of electric utility power.[161]

Source: power-technology.com, http://www.power-technology.com/contractor_ images/ pauwels/5_Mobile-substation.jpg.

Figure 23. Trailer-Mounted Mobile Substation.

Storm-Specific Readiness

Readiness activities that take place in response to the approach of a specific storm include:

- **Facilitating employee evacuation and reentry**
- **Securing emergency fuel contracts for vehicles and generators**
- **Supplying logistics to staging areas**

Facilitating Employee Evacuation and Reentry

When an area has been evacuated for a hurricane, the first step in restoring power has to be allowing essential personnel, especially utility repair crews, back into the damaged area. Without an exemption from an evacuation order, restoration is delayed. Utilities work with local government to secure exemptions from evacuation orders, so that restoration of damaged systems can begin as soon as it is safe to re-enter an area. At least one major utility has signed memoranda of understanding with city mayors in vulnerable areas to ensure that critical employees have access to the areas where they are most needed in a restoration effort.

With proper planning, emergency permits or waivers from other types of regulation may also help to speed recovery. For example, some utilities have sought waivers for the transportation of fuel so that fuel for emergency generation and other uses can be brought into the affected area quickly. After Hurricanes Gustav and Ike hit the Entergy service area in rapid succession, the company was able to obtain special highway permits to allow the after-dark transportation of oversized loads of steel tubing to repair lattice towers.[162] Utilities affected by Katrina obtained a waiver from FERC that exempted them from reporting requirements, enabling them to focus more fully on the restoration efforts.[163]

Obtaining exemptions, permits, and waivers typically involves a great deal of time and paperwork. Oftentimes, they cannot be executed quickly enough to be of any practical value in an emergency situation unless the process is started well before the emergency begins. Utilities are more likely to find such tools useful if they have become familiar with the procedures, paperwork, and contacts before the event of an emergency.

Securing Emergency Fuel Contracts for Vehicles and Generators

The availability of vehicle fuel is a major concern for companies restoring electricity during an outage. During Hurricane Katrina, the average daily fuel consumption by utilities in the region was about 80,000 gallons, and the peak one-day consumption was more than 110,000 gallons.[164] Fuel may become scarce during energy emergencies, though, and if it does, wholesalers may go on allocation. When a wholesaler is on allocation, it will not sell fuel to a customer who does not have a pre-existing purchasing contract, so utilities that have purchasing contracts in place in advance of the hurricane season are less likely to run into fuel shortages during their restoration efforts.

Most of the companies reported having fuel contracts in place to supply emergency vehicles and small portable generators necessary to power some basic operations and IT sites. At least one company reported that its emergency plans arrange for skid tanks – portable fuel tanks used for refueling vehicles – to be delivered to pre-determined locations following a storm.

Supplying Logistics to Staging Areas

By necessity, electric utilities' hurricane preparedness plans include provisions for creating staging areas for the restoration effort. Staging areas provide work crews with a base of operations, and they are typically set up near affected infrastructure. It is in a staging area that personnel obtain supplies, maps to work sites, vehicle fuel (generally stored in skid tanks), meals, showers, and other basic necessities. Staging areas may also offer computer, Internet, and other communications equipment and capabilities.[165]

The utilities reported that they plan staging areas well in advance of approaching storms to ensure that sufficient food, water, and other supplies for personnel are available. Lessons learned from previous hurricanes have led some utilities to change or expand these plans. In some cases, utilities had found that they did not have enough staging areas, or that the staging areas were too far from affected infrastructure, and personnel were required to drive long distances over storm-damaged terrain to reach the areas.

In response to Hurricane Ike, CenterPoint Energy set up four staging areas around the Houston/Galveston area. As the restoration effort grew and took shape, the number of staging areas swelled to 11.[166] Managing logistics at staging areas is a significant effort. During one week, September 13-21, 2008, Oncor Electric delivery's staging areas consumed 69,468 bottles of water, 82,158 bottles of Gatorade, 290,325 pounds of ice, and 76,000 gallons of fuel, as well as 50,000 meals. Setting up, operating, and tearing down the staging area alone required the efforts of 219 Oncor employees, along with 705 contractors.[167]

Mississippi Power prepared for Hurricane Katrina by identifying more than 100 possible staging areas, and outlining plans for how they would be used. Looking after the basic needs of the workers was given as much consideration as providing the necessary supplies for the restoration. Of the 30 staging areas that were in service at the peak of the restoration, 18 were used for meals, lodging, refueling, materials, showers, and parking. The other 12 sites were used as material lay- down yards. At that point, nearly 11,000 people were housed, 93,000 pounds of clothing was laundered, 32,000 meals were served in a single day, and 65 buses were put into service. All of this was possible because of a previous arrangement with a logistics vendor that provided tents, caterers, portable toilets, showers, and dumpsters, and all supplies were in place three days before the storm made landfall. The price tag for this equipment and logistical support was $7 million.[168]

Recently, self-sufficiency has become an increasingly important consideration in planning for storm recovery. Plans must assume that in emergency conditions, local suppliers will not be able to meet the needs of restoration crews, and backup plans are necessary to ensure that staging areas are adequately supplied.

HARDENING AND RESILIENCY CONCLUSIONS

Refiners, petroleum product pipeline and terminal operators, and the electric utilities serving them in the Gulf Coast and Southeast have all been active in hardening and resiliency. This report identifies energy industry investment in hardening and resiliency and provides an organizational framework for documenting those efforts. A total of 33 activities are organized in Table 9 by Hardening – flood protection, wind protections, and modernization – and Resiliency – general readiness and storm-specific readiness.

The focus of the report is on efforts to mitigate petroleum product shortages in the Southeast after a hurricane. Specific energy segments were targeted and investment in hardening and resiliency has been focused on the damage most prevalent in the energy segment.

The refinery and pipeline industry suffers the greatest damage from storm surge and flooding that accompany hurricanes making landfall in the Gulf. Constructing flood protection structures (e.g., floodwalls, levees, and berms) or raising the height of existing structures, and elevating critical control rooms and pump stations above flood stage have been the primary efforts. Investment in new technologies and equipment that both modernize and harden their operations appears to be more robust that their investment in wind protection.

In terms of resiliency, the refinery and pipeline/terminal operators appear most interested in preparedness activities – maintaining minimum tank volumes, staging command vehicles and portable generators, coordinating priority restoration and employee evacuation exemption and/or reentry. There is no regulation of storm hardening for refineries and pipelines, only industry standards and best practices (e.g., inspection cycles) that industry follows to protect its assets.

Table 9. Summary Findings of Energy Hardening and Resiliency Activities

Industry Activities			Refineries/ Pipelines	Electric T&D
Hardening	Flood Protection	Building/strengthening berms, levees, and floodwalls	√	
		Elevating substations/control rooms/pump stations	√	√
		Relocating/constructing new lines and facilities	√	√
	Wind Protection	Securing cooling towers	√	
		Improving tank integrity	√	
		Protecting cabling	√	
		Protecting retail outlets	√	
		Upgrading damaged poles and structures		√
		Strengthening poles with guy wires		√
		Burying power lines underground		√
	Modernization	Upgrading electrical systems	√	
		Installing/utilizing cogeneration	√	
		Enhancing IT and telecommunications	√	
		deploying sensors and control technology		√
		Installing asset databases/tools	√	√
Resiliency	General Readiness	Conducting hurricane preparedness planning and training	√	√
		Complying with inspection protocols	√	√
		Managing vegetation		√
		Participating in mutual assistance groups		√
		Improving employee communications and tracking	√	
		Installing redundant communications	√	
		Procuring mobile command vehicles	√	
		Purchasing/leasing portable generators	√	
		Pre-positioning and pre-wiring portable generators	√	
		Securing alternate sources of gas supplies	√	
		Purchasing or leasing mobile transformers and substations		√
		Procuring spare T&D equipment		√
	Storm-Specific Readiness	Maintaining minimum tank volumes	√	
		Wrapping/protecting pumps and motors	√	
		Facilitating employee evacuation and reentry	√	√
		Coordinating priority restoration and waivers	√	
		Securing emergency fuel contracts		√
		Supplying logistics to staging areas		√

Electric utilities have invested in significant construction projects to elevate T&D substations above the flood plain and relocate distribution operations offices and control equipment further inland to avoid salt-water flooding. But these investments are limited by comparison with the level of effort required for wind protection. Electric utilities suffer the most extensive damage from extreme hurricane winds in the Gulf and Southeast and the public utility commissions in these States have enacted rulemakings on utility storm hardening. Utility investments replace thousands of distribution poles and dozens of transmission towers annually as well as strengthening those poles with guy wires. Burying power lines is not considered a complete solution, particularly in areas likely to flood, as the resulting complications can keep these underground lines out of service longer than overhead lines.

Electric utilities have invested manpower and funds in hurricane preparedness planning, pole inspection programs, vegetation management, voluntary collaboration in regional mutual assistance groups and supplying logistics to deployed utility employees. They have acquired fleets of mobile substations and transformers and stock spare equipment necessary for rebuilding after major hurricanes.

Energy companies will continue to make investments and pursue technological solutions. Appendix A highlights selected advances in technology that contribute to hardening and resiliency efforts.

APPENDIX A. SELECTED HARDENING AND RESILIENCY TECHNOLOGY INNOVATIONS

A perusal of the various hardening and resiliency measures taken by the energy sector reveals a number of technological advances. These innovations have allowed utilities and petroleum companies to further the cause of storm hardening and resiliency in ways that would have been impossible until recent years. Although many of them are communications and IT-based, advances in materials and construction methods have allowed improvements in areas as fundamental as flood wall and utility pole design. The application of some of these innovations is referenced in the petroleum and electricity sections of this report. What follows is a summary review of hardening and resiliency technology that has been developed and has entered (or is soon to enter) the marketplace.

- **Petroleum infrastructure innovations**
  - **HESCO Concertainers**
  - **Upgraded Modular Transformers**
- **Electricity infrastructure innovations**
  - **Phasor Measurement Units (PMUs)**
  - **Composite Utility Poles**
  - **Infrared Thermography Power Line Inspection**
  - **High-Temperature Superconductor Power Transmission Cables**
  - **Utility Pole Reinforcements**
  - **Smart Grid Integration**
  - **Electric Distribution Recloser Advances**

Petroleum Infrastructure Innovations

HESCO Concertainers

Developed by HESCO Bastion Ltd, the Concertainer is a collapsible, welded, steel-mesh, cage- like framework lined with non-woven fabric and filled with locally available material such as rocks, rubble, sand, gravel, or soil. It is delivered to the site flat-packed on standard timber skids or pallets.[169] The Floodline is a special geotextile-lined unit for use in flood-protection that has been developed to reduce permeability of the wall when filled.[170] In the event of a flood warning, HESCO Concertainer units can be deployed quickly and easily to add height to an existing levee without the need for specialist tradesmen or equipment, making it ideal for emergency response (see Figure 24). After Hurricane Katrina, ConocoPhillips deployed some of these units around the perimeter of its Belle Chasse refinery and the USACE installed the units to close breaches in canal levees.[171] USACE has recently decided to develop a strategic plan for stockpiling Concertainer units across the United States. This new program will offer rapid flood protection to residents in a state of emergency.

Upgraded Modular Transformers

Oak Ridge National Laboratory and Waukesha Electric Systems are developing technology that will allow the construction of modular transformers with higher power density for use in compact substations and mobile power transformer systems. The modular system components will include protective equipment such as breakers and surge arresters, switchgear, monitoring, and cooling systems. They will be mounted on trailers for highway transportation (see Figure 25), and will be designed for flexibility and ease of connection. These innovations will offer improvements over current modular transformer technology, which has a number of limitations.

Source: HESCO. http://www.hescobastion.com/us_civil/images/projects/fargo_mid2.jpg, accessed May 7, 2010.

Figure 24. HESCO Floodline Concertainer Installation.

Source:http://www.ornl.gov/sci/electricdelivery/pdfs/DECC%20OE%20Overview.pdf, accessed June 28, 2010.

Figure 25. Trailer-Mounted Mobile Transformer.

According to manufacturers, the new generation of higher power density transformers will have higher voltages, increased operational flexibility and insulation systems that can withstand higher operating temperatures. Higher-flux steels will be used to increase the power density of transformers and reduce their size. By increasing operating flux density, it may be possible to reduce weight, volume, and price by as much as 25 percent. The use of higher-temperature insulation using a combination of plastics and cellulose may allow size and weight reductions of up to 30 percent.[172]

Electricity Infrastructure Innovations

Phasor Measurement Units (PMUs)

PMUs are instruments that measure the voltage, current, and frequency on an electrical grid to determine the health of the system. A PMU is essentially a digital recorder with synchronized capability. It can provide real-time information about power system events in its area, and multiple PMUs can enable coordinated system-wide measurements. PMUs can also time-stamp, record, and store the phasor measurements of power system events. They are ideal for monitoring and controlling the dynamic performance of a power system, especially during high- stress operating conditions.[173] This enables them to provide improved system restoration and event analysis during a major disturbance such as a hurricane. Entergy participated in a demonstration of PMUs in 2008.

Composite Utility Poles

Composite utility poles are made from fiberglass reinforced polymer composite material. They provide an alternative to traditional wood, steel, or concrete poles, and have several advantages over other materials. The composite poles are:

- Lighter
- More impact-resistant
- Resistant to rot or decay
- Free of toxic preservatives
- Non-conductive
- Resistant to woodpecker or insect damage
- Virtually maintenance free

A specific advantage over steel poles for coastal regions is that they are corrosion resistant and will not rust.[174] Although composite poles have existed for many years, cost and susceptibility to ultraviolet light have prevented widespread commercialization. In recent years, however, material costs have come down due to advances in fiberglass technology and ultraviolet issues have been addressed by advances in polymer chemistry.[175] Composite poles have typically been used for distribution lines (see Figure 26), but composite transmission poles (70-to-80 foot tall) are also becoming available.[176]

Source: EPL Composite Solutions Ltd, http://www.eplcompositesolutions.co.uk/images/ pole1.jpg, accessed May 7, 2010.

Figure 26. Composite Distribution Pole.

Source: http://www.ir55.com/images/12570998777new-12.jpg, accessed June 27, 2010.

Figure 27. Infrared Substation Scan.

Infrared Thermography Power Line Inspection

Utilities are increasingly using infrared technology to scan and identify problems with transmission lines and other electrical equipment. When components of electrical systems begin to fail, a common symptom is a significant temperature difference between ailing components and their surroundings (see Figure 27 identifying a potentially defective substation component).[177]

By using infrared technology, utilities can perform fast and efficient preventative maintenance on large areas of transmission circuits. Routine infrared scans of critical equipment can help avoid emergency restoration efforts by identifying problems prior to failure.[178]

High-Temperature Superconductor Power Transmission Cables

High-Temperature Superconductor (HTS) Power Transmission Cable is a high-current, second- generation superconducting wire for coils and motors.[179] HTS cables enable the transmission and distribution of more energy more effectively, and with minimal environmental and community impact.

HTS wire is installed underground and can conduct 150 times the electrical current of copper of the same dimensions. The inherently low impedance of this cable assembly enables enhanced control of power flows over the surrounding grid network. Liquid nitrogen is used as a dielectric coolant to maintain the HTS wire at its operating temperature, eliminating the oil used in conventional underground power cables.

Case Study: First HTS Grid Demonstration

The world's first high-temperature superconductor power transmission cable system in a commercial power grid was energized on April 22, 2008 at the Holbrook substation on Long Island, New York. The 138 kV, 2,000-foot cable system, the longest superconducting cable in the world, includes three phases connected to the Long Island Power Authority's grid through six outdoor terminations.

Source: American Superconductor, http://www.amsc.com/pdf/HTSC_AN_0109_A4_FINAL.pdf, accessed June 27, 2010.

Utility Pole Reinforcements

Wood utility poles may need additional strength to storm-harden a system. Osmose Utility Services, Inc. has developed the ET-Truss, an "extended and tapered" wood utility pole truss system that is engineered to increase the strength and bending capacity of wood poles, while costing a third of the price, or less, of a complete pole replacement.[180] The truss system comprises a galvanized steel reinforcing truss which is secured to a pole by galvanized steel bands. By installing the ET-Truss, bending capacity of a wood pole, as measured by NESC, can be increased significantly. A specific ET-Truss model is chosen to meet strength requirements and overloaded conditions and can usually be installed with no disruption to service (see Figure 28).

Source: http://www.osmoseutilities.com/content/pages/et-truss, accessed April 12, 2010.

Figure 28. Osmose ET-Truss.

Smart Grid Integration

Smart Grid is a blanket term that refers to the application of advances in technology and networking abilities to improve the reliability and efficiency of the electric transmission and distribution grid. Major components of a Smart Grid include automation and two-way communication between components of an electric supply system. This includes the introduction of smart meters that can not only receive data but send information back to utilities. A smarter grid is able to respond more rapidly to outage occurrences and possibly even "self-heal" in the event of a major disturbance.

Under the American Reinvestment and Recovery Act, a number of companies have been awarded Smart Grid projects. For example, CenterPoint Energy has been awarded a $200 million DOE stimulus grant for its smart meter and Smart Grid projects. Of these funds, $50 million will be used to begin building a self-healing Smart Grid that will use smart meters, power line sensors, remote switches, and other automated equipment to improve power reliability and restoration in greater Houston. In the event of large outages, such as those caused by a hurricane, the Smart Grid will first employ self-healing techniques to restore power to as much of the system as possible. Damage to the system can then be diagnosed and mapped system- wide. Using that information, CenterPoint Energy will be able to expedite a full restoration.

In many cases, the time to restore power through the Smart Grid in CenterPoint Energy's service area is projected to be a fraction of the current averages. The initial Smart Grid deployment is expected to be completed in 2013.[181]

Electric Distribution Recloser Advances

An electric recloser senses and interrupts currents, and automatically restores service after a momentary outage. S&C Electric Company has developed advanced recloser technology called IntelliRupter PulseCloser that provides an alternative to conventional automatic circuit reclosers and won an R&D100 award in 2009.[182]IntelliRupter is designed to operate with advanced distribution automation functions, including SCADA systems, and provides better segmentation and coordination than conventional reclosers. A conventional recloser tests the line through repeatedly applying damaging fault current to equipment. In contrast, IntelliRupter utilizes PulseClosing™ Technology, a unique means for verifying that the line is clear of faults before initiating a close (i.e., shut) operation. PulseClosing™ greatly reduces stress on system components, as well as voltage sags experienced by customers upstream of a fault (see the recloser installed atop a distribution pole in Figure 29.

Source: S&C Electric Company, IntelliRupter® PulseCloser, http://www.sandc.com/products/intell irupter/default.asp, accessed June 28, 2010.

Figure 29. Installed IntelliRupter Recloser.

End Notes

[1] NIST, *Performance of Physical Structures in Hurricane Katrina and Hurricane Rita: A Reconnaissance Report*, June 2006, http://www.bfrl.nist.gov/investigations/pubs/NIST_TN_1476_ExecSum.pdf, accessed April 22, 2010.

[2] *ComputerWorld*. http://www.computerworld.com/s/article/104477/After_Katrina_Valero_Energy_turns_to_satellite_communications, accessed May 28, 2010.

[3] http://www.gopower.com/products/generators/diesel/1/1000-10000000/1000%20kW%20and%20Up%20Diesel%20Generators, accessed July 1, 2010.

[4] Mihelick, P. J., "Colonial Pipeline, One Pipeline Company's Response to Hurricanes Gustav and Ike," 2009 Tulane Engineering Forum, http://www.tulane.edu/~sse/FORUM_2009/program/, accessed January 20, 2010.

[5] http://www.myfloridahouse.gov/Sections/Documents/loaddoc.aspx?FileName=_h7121er.doc&DocumentType=Bill&BillNumber=7121&Session=2006, accessed January 16, 2010.

[6] EEI, "Underground vs. Overhead Distribution Wires – Issues to Consider," http://www.eei.org/ourissues/ electricitydistribution/Documents/UnderVSOver.pdf, accessed May 12, 2010.

[7] ESRI, http://www.esri.com/news/releases/09_3qtr/hurricane.html, accessed April 22, 2010.

[8] Hurricanes Katrina and Rita made landfall within one month of each other in 2005 and Hurricanes Gustav and Ike made landfall within two weeks of each other in 2008. All of these were major hurricanes, defined as are Category 3 or higher with winds exceeding 111 miles per hour. http://www.nhc.noaa.gov/sshws_table.shtml?large, accessed May 17, 2010.

[9] *Comparing the Impacts of the 2005 and 2008 Hurricanes on U.S. Energy Infrastructure* (February 2009) is available at http://www.oe.netl.doe.gov/docs/HurricaneComp0508r2.pdf.

[10] An allocation limits contractual customers to receipt of a specific percent of what they normally receive at the terminal, as determined by the terminal operator, though typically based on an average of the previous 12 months.

[11] Summer gasoline grades vary by State:

- Florida/Louisiana/North Carolina/Tennessee 7.8 RVP conventional
- Alabama/Georgia7.0 RVP conventional
- Texas 7.8 RVP and partial RFG (El Paso 7.0)
- Mississippi/South Carolina 9.0 RVP conventional

http://www.epa.gov/otaq/regs/fuels/420b10018.pdf and http://www.epa.gov/otaq/rfg/whereyoulive.htm.

[12] Electricity is usually restored quickly relative to damage from storm surge and flooding. In 2005 and 2008, certain utilities suffered extensive damage to their distribution networks, delaying power restoration for weeks.

[13] Atkinson, W., *Equities Magazine*, in NASDAQ Utility Infrastructure: Addressing the Aging Electric and Water Systems, http://www.nasdaq.com/newscontent/20100204/utility_infrastructure_addressing_the_aging_electric_and_water_systems.aspx?storyid=20100204233110equit#ixzz0saG5S6Go, accessed February 18, 2010.

[14] Stock Interview. http://www.stockinterview.com/News/03042007/molybdenum-energy-US-pipelines.html , accessed February 18, 2010.

[15] Marathon's Garyville Refinery in Louisiana.

[16] http://www.texasalmanac.com/history/highlights/oil/, accessed June 26, 2010.

[17] Blake, E.S., *et. al.*, "The Deadliest, Costliest, and Most Intense United States Tropical Cyclones from 1851 to 2006," NOAA Technical Memorandum NWS TPC-5, April 2007, http://www.nhc.noaa.gov/pdf/NWS-TPC-5.pdf, accessed June 5, 2010.

[18] MATCO Services, Inc., Hurricane/Water Damage Inspection Services, http://www.matcoinc.com/failure-analysis/hurricanewater-damage, accessed June 7, 2010.

[19] Marshall, T., P.E., On the Performance of Buildings in Hurricanes: A Study for the Saffir-Simspon Scale Committee, October 18, 2009, http://www.nhc.noaa.gov/testing/sshws/SSHWS-Marshall.pdf, accessed June 4, 2010.

[20] NOAA, National Weather Service, National Hurricane Center, "Storm Surge Scales and Storm Surge Forecasting," http://www.nhc.noaa.gov/sshws_statement.shtml, accessed June 5, 2010.

[21] NOAA defines eyewall as "An organized band or ring of cumulonimbus clouds that surround the eye, or light-wind center of a tropical cyclone." http://www.nhc.noaa.gov/aboutgloss.shtml#e, accessed June 5, 2010.

[22] Subra, W., "Hurricane Gustav Damage Assessment," Louisiana Environmental Action Network, September 7, 2008, http://leanweb.org/campaigns/hurricanes-gustav-and-ike/hurricane-gustav-damage-assessment-2.html, accessed June 4, 2010.

[23] For example, see the National Infrastructure Advisory Council, Critical Infrastructure Resilience: Final Report and Recommendations. September 8, 2009, http://www.dhs.gov/xlibrary/assets/niac/niac_critical_infrastructure_resilience.pdf, accessed July 1, 2010.

[24] Calculated from EIA, http://www.eia.gov/oil_gas/petroleum/data_publications/refinery_capacity_data/ refcapacity.html, accessed June 11, 2010.

[25] More details on refinery shut down and restoration periods for each storm are provided in Appendix Tables A-5 through A-8 in *Comparing the Impacts of the 2005 and 2008 Hurricanes on U.S. Energy Infrastructure* (February 2009), http://www.oe.netl.doe.gov/docs/HurricaneComp0508r2.pdf.

[26] Some refineries have electric utility substation(s) inside their fence.

[27] U.S. Army Corps of Engineers (USACE), "Management Measures Digital Library: Floodwalls, Levees, and Dams." http://www.iwr.usace.army.mil/index.php, accessed April 28, 2010.

[28] Known as the "Ike Dike." http://www.semp.us/publications/biot_reader.php?BiotID=601.

[29] U.S. Army Corps of Engineers (USACE), "Greater New Orleans Hurricane and Storm Damage Risk Reduction System Facts and Figures," http://www.mvn.usace.army.mil/hps2/pdf/June_web_2010.pdf, accessed June 14, 2010.

[30] Entergy Texas, Inc., "Economic Trends – March 26, 2009: State of Texas," http://www.entergy-texas.com/content/economic_development/docs/area_economic_update.pdf, accessed April 22, 2010.

[31] Kennedy, S., "Plant Services names its Plant of the Year," http://www.plantservices.com/articles/2006/259.html, accessed May 15, 2010.

[32] Fowler, T., "Houston-area refineries say they're prepared," *Houston Chronicle*, Sept. 21, 2005, http://www.chron.com/disp/story.mpl/special/05/rita/3362796.html, accessed June 5, 2010.

[33] BP, *Frontiers*, Issue 21, April 2008: Global Insights, http://www.bp.com/sectiongenericarticle.do?categoryId=9023212&contentId=7043102, and Lang, K., BP Vice President for the Gulf of Mexico, "After the Storm…" Undated presentation, http://www.rice.edu/energy/publications/docs/KennyLang_katrina.pdf, accessed April 22, 2010.

[34] ExxonMobil. "Overview of ExxonMobil storm preparation," http://www.exxonmobil.com/corporate/community_safety_er_storm_preparation.aspx; and http://www.exxonmobil.com/corporate/news_features_20090227_storms.aspx, accessed June 12, 2010

[35] Chevron, *Developing Partnerships: 2008 Corporate Responsibility Report*, https://chevron.com/globalissues/corporateresponsibility/2008/documents/Chevron_CR_Report_2008.pdf p. 22, p. 24, accessed May 15, 2010.

[36] Jefferson Parish, State of Louisiana, *Jefferson Parish Post Katrina Flood Protection Plan Update: 3 Years Later*, September 17, 2008. http://www.jeffparish.net/downloads/3753/6386-KatrinaFloodProtectionUpdate3YearsLater.pdf, accessed May 15, 2010.

[37] Cooling Towers of Texas. "Fan Lock," http://www.coolingtowersoftexas.com/fanlock.html, accessed April 22, 2010.

[38] Valero Port Arthur, ExxonMobil Beaumont, and Motiva Port Arthur were cited in NIST Technical Note 1476, *Performance of Physical Structures in Hurricane Katrina and Hurricane Rita: A Reconnaissance Report*, June 2006, http://www.bfrl.nist.gov/investigations/pubs/NIST_TN_1476_ExecSum.pdf, accessed April 22, 2010.

[39] Carucci, V., "Changes to API 650, Eleventh Edition – Welded Steel Tanks for Oil Storage," *Carmagen eNews Report,* Carmagen Engineering Inc. March 2010, accessed June 22, 2010.

[40] National Electrical Manufacturers Association, Metal Cable Tray Systems, http://www.nema.org/stds/ve1.cfm, accessed April 13, 2010; and NEMA News, "NEMA Publishes VE 1-2009 Metal Cable Tray Systems," http://www.nema.org/media/pr/20091008a.cfm, accessed April 13, 2010.

[41] NIST Technical Note 1476, *Performance of Physical Structures in Hurricane Katrina and Hurricane Rita: A Reconnaissance Report*, June 2006, http://www.bfrl.nist.gov/investigations/pubs/NIST_TN_1476_ExecSum.pdf, accessed April 22, 2010.

[42] *Ibid.*

[43] DOE, Distributed Energy Program, "Protecting Critical Energy Infrastructure and Helping Communities Recover from Disaster with Distributed Energy Assets," December 27, 2005, http://www.sentech.org/pdfs/DE%20Protect%20and%20Recover.pdf, accessed June 22, 2010.

[44] Calculated from Energy Velocity data retrieval, December 12, 2009.

[45] *Ibid.*

[46] DOE/EIA Glossary, http://www.eia.doe.gov/glossary/glossary_c.htm, accessed February 18, 2010.

[47] Calculated from EIA-861 data, accessed February 18, 2010.

[48] "After Katrina, Valero Energy turns to satellite communications," *ComputerWorld*, September 8, 2005, http://www.computerworld.com/s/article/104477/After_Katrina_Valero_Energy_turns_to_ satellite_communications, accessed June 22, 2010.

[49] ExxonMobil, "Overview of ExxonMobil storm preparation," http://www.exxonmobil.com/corporate/community_safety_er_storm_preparation.aspx, accessed June 22, 2010.

[50] NTSB, Supervisory Control and Data Acquisition (SCADA) in Liquid Pipelines, Safety Study NTSB/SS-05/02, November 29, 2005, http://www.ntsb.gov/publictn/2005/ss0502.pdf, accessed May 17, 2010.

[51] BP, http://www.bp.com/liveassets/bp_internet/globalbp/STAGING/global_assets /BPM_05two_pipelines.pdf, accessed May 17, 2010.

[52] ESRI, "GIS Technology for Disasters and Emergency Management," May 2000, http://www.esri.com/library/whitepapers/pdfs/disastermgmt.pdf, accessed May 17, 2010.

[53] Xterprise, "ExxonMobil Global Location System (GLS) Provides Detailed Tracking of High Value Mobile Assets," undated, http://www.xterprise.com/Files/Cases/SuccessStory_XOM.pdf, accessed May 11, 2010.

[54] "Impact of New PHMSA Control Room Management Rules," *Pipeline & Gas Journal*, April 2010, http://pipelineandgasjournal.com/impact-new-phmsa-control-room-management ?page=show, accessed June 22, 2010.

[55] Railroad Commission of Texas, "About RRC," http://www.rrc.state.tx.us/about/index.php, accessed June 22, 2010.

[56] Texas Commission on Environmental Quality, Agency Response to Events, Spills, http://www.tceq.state.tx.us/response/spills.html, accessed June 22, 2010

[57] NPRA, Hurricane Security Operations, May 31, 2006, http://www.npra.org/files/hurricane_security_operations.pdf , accessed June 22, 2010.

[58] ExxonMobil, http://www.exxonmobil.com/corporate/files/news_pub_lamp_2009-2.pdf, accessed May 4, 2010.

[59] ExxonMobil, "What we do when storms hit hard," http://www.exxonmobil.com/corporate/news_features_20090601_storm_prep.aspx, accessed May 4, 2010.

[60] Shell, http://www.shell.us/home/content/usa/aboutshell/media motiva _prepared/onshore/#wrapper, accessed May 5, 2010.

[61] PlantServices, Plant Services names its Plant of the Year, http://www.plantservices.com/articles/2006/259.html, accessed May 10, 2010.

[62] ExxonMobil, Emergency preparedness and response, http://www.exxonmobil.com/NA-English/about_where_ref_bt_emergprep.aspx, accessed May 4, 2010.

[63] A refinery turnaround is a planned, periodic shutdown of one or more refinery processing units (or possibly the entire refinery) to perform maintenance, inspection, and repair of equipment

and to replace process materials and equipment that have worn out or broken, in order to ensure safe and efficient operations. See EIA, www.eia.doe.gov/oiaf/servicerpt/refinery_outages/ SROOG200701.pdf, accessed June 1, 2010.

[64] API, Refinery Turnaround, http://www.api.org/aboutoilgas/sectors/refining/refinery-turnaround.cfm, accessed May 18, 2010.

[65] API, IPC Programs in Detail, http://www.api.org/certifications/icp/programs/index.cfm, accessed May 18, 2010.

[66] NCPCM. http://www.ncpcm.org/pdf/ASTManual012010.pdf, accessed May 4, 2010.

[67] PHMSA. http://primis.phmsa.dot.gov/comm/InspectionEnforcement.htm, accessed January 13, 2010.

[68] CFR 195.412 Inspection of rights-of-way and crossings under navigable waters (last amended June 28, 1994), http://ecfr.gpoaccess.gov/cgi/t/text/text-idx?c=ecfr;sid=d6823325054b0559253dee57ebcc3067;rgn=div5;view=text;node=49%3A3.1.1.1.7;idno=49;cc=ecfr#49:3.1.1.1.7.6.21.10, accessed January 13, 2010.

[69] *Ibid.*

[70] http://www.bp.com/sectiongenericarticle.do?categoryId=9023212&contentId=7043102 and http://www.rice.edu/energy/publications/docs/KennyLang_katrina.pdf, accessed January 13, 2010.

[71] *EnewsBuilder*, http://www.enewsbuilder.net/aopl/e_article000452974.cfm?x=b11,0,w, accessed May 17, 2010.

[72] Marathon Oil. http://www.marathoncares.com/go/site/1772/, accessed May 6, 2010.

[73] ExxonMobil, http://www.exxonmobil.com/corporate/community_safety_er_storm_preparation.aspx, accessed May 4, 2010.

[74] Shell, http://www.shell.us/home/content/usa/aboutshell/media_center/storm_center/shell_motiva_prepared/onshore/, accessed May 5, 2010.

[75] Chevron. http://www.cpchem.us/phone_numbers.html, accessed May 5, 2010.

[76] Rissler, J., Texas Railroad Commission, personal communication, February 24, 2010.

[77] Ground Control, Katrina Case Study, http://www.groundcontrol.com/katrina.htm, accessed May 18, 2010.

[78] PHMSA, Hurricane Response, http://www.phmsa.dot.gov, accessed May 18, 2010.

[79] NCS GETS. http://gets.ncs.gov/program_info.html , accessed May 4, 2010.

[80] Statement of Dr. Peter M. Fonash, Deputy Manager, National Communications System, Before the Senate Committee on Homeland Security and Governmental Affairs, February 6, 2006. http://hsgac.senate.gov/public/, accessed May 4, 2010.

[81] NCS WPS, http://wps.ncs.gov/program_info.html, accessed May 4, 2010.

[82] Clegg Industries built the unit for Chevron; General Truck Body built units for BP and Valero. Many other vehicle manufacturers are active in producing and delivering such vehicles.

[83] Riecher, A., "Assembling Your Apparatus," *Industrial Fire World*, Vol 22 Number 5, May 2007, http://www.fireworld.com/ifw_articles/assembling_090107.php, accessed May 11, 2010.

[84] *Ibid.*

[85] National Fire Protection Association, Standard 110 "Standard for Emergency and Standby Power Systems" (2005 edition), http://www.nfpa.org/catalog/product.asp?pid=11010&order%5Fsrc=B484, accessed April 13, 2010.

[86] This price is typical of multiple dealers. http://www.gopower.com/products/generators/diesel/1/1000-10000000/1000%20kW%20and%20Up%20Diesel%20Generators, accessed July 1, 2010.

[87] Kohler, http://www.kohlerpower.com/rental/library/case_study.htm?fn=cs_conaco.xml§ionNumber=28161, accessed May 17, 2010.

[88] Mihelick, P.J., "Colonial Pipeline, One Pipeline Company's Response to Hurricanes Gustav and Ike," 2009 Tulane Engineering Forum, http://www.tulane.edu/~sse/FORUM_2009/program/, accessed January 20, 2010.

[89] Shell. http://www.shell.us/home/content/usa/aboutshell/media, accessed May 5, 2010.

[90] ExxonMobil. http://www.exxonmobil.com/corporate/community_safety_er_storm_preparation.aspx, accessed May 4, 2010.

[91] ExxonMobil. http://www.exxonmobil.com/corporate/news_features_20090601_storm_prep.aspx, accessed May 4, 2010.

[92] http://www.myfloridahouse.gov/Sections/Documents/loaddoc.aspx?FileName=_h7121er.doc&DocumentType=Bil l&BillNumber=7121&Session=2006, accessed January 16, 2010. Not every retail outlet is required to have generators. The Florida rule applies to companies operating a certain number of stations in populated areas served by a specific number of stations.

[93] Tampa Bay Online, TBO.com, "How prepared is the Tampa area for storm season?" May 28, 2010, http://www2.tbo.com/content/2010/may/28/how-prepared-tampa-bay-storm-season/c_1/, accessed May 22, 2010.

[94] http://www.uigi.com/hydrogen.html, accessed May 31, 2010 and Chevron, http://www.chevron.com/products/sitelets/pascagoula/refiningprocess/proccrude.aspx, accessed May 22, 2010.

[95] http://www.uigi.com/nitrogen.html, accessed May 31, 2010 and http://www.southtektalk.com/2010/01/nitrogen-use-with-oil-platforms-and.html, accessed May 22, 2010.

[96] http://www.uigi.com/oxygen.html, accessed May 31, 2010.

[97] http://www.thefreelibrary.com/Air+Liquide+America+Celebrates+SMR+Start-Up+in+Corpus+Christi.-a053195109, accessed May 22, 2010.

[98] http://news.thomasnet.com/companystory/Air-Products-to-Build-New-Hydrogen-Production-Facility-Linked-to-Pipeline-Network-to-Supply-Marathon-s-Garyville-La-Refinery-Expansion-515303, accessed July1, 2010.

[99] Peltier, PE, Dr. R., "Port Arthur II Integrated Hydrogen/Cogeneration Facility, Port Arthur, Texas," *Power*, September 15, 2007, http://www.powermag.com/gas/Port-Arthur-II-Integrated -HydrogenCogeneration-Facility-Port-Arthur-Texas_408.html, accessed May 22, 2010.

[100] http://www.universalpegasus.com/projects.php?page=onshore_pipeline, accessed May 31, 2010.

[101] http://www.api650.com/, accessed May 15, 2010.

[102] Petroleum Equipment Institute. http://www.pei.org/PublicationsResources/ Recommended PracticesExams/%20RP800/tabid/106/Default.aspx, accessed May 15, 2010.

[103] Flowserve, Dave DePaolis, communication June 2, 2010.

[104] State of Louisiana, Standard Operating Procedure, Statewide Credentialing/Access Program. http://www.lsp.org/pdf/lscap.pdf, accessed May 15, 2010.

[105] WageHourBlog, http://www.wagehourblog.com/uploads/file/HR%20Guide%20for%20Hurricane%20and%20Disaster%20Preparatio n.pdf, accessed May 4, 2010.

[106] NACS Online, http://www.nacsonline.com/NACS/Magazine/PastIssues/2008/November2008/Pages/Feature1.aspx, accessed May 18, 2010.

[107] PHMSA. http://www.phmsa.dot.gov/prepare-respond, accessed May 18, 2010.

[108] NIST Technical Note 1476, *Performance of Physical Structures in Hurricane Katrina and Hurricane Rita: A Reconnaissance Report*, June 2006, http://www.bfrl.nist.gov/investigations/pubs/NIST_TN_1476_ExecSum.pdf, accessed April 22, 2010.

[109] EEI. Underground vs. Overhead Distribution Wires – Issues to Consider. http://www.eei.org/ourissues/electricitydistribution/Documents/UnderVSOver.pdf, accessed May 12, 2010.

[110] FPSC Storm Hardening Activities, http://www.floridapsc.com/utilities/electricgas/eiproject/, accessed June 10, 2010.

[111] LPSC Docket Search Page, Docket No. R-30821, R-30820, and U-31075. https://p8.lpsc.org/Workplace/Search.jsp, accessed June 10, 2010.

[112] PUCT Rulemakings 34495, 34737, 37387, 37472, and 37475, http://www.puc.state.tx.us/rules/rulemake/, accessed June 10, 2010.

[113] NOAA, http://www.nhc.noaa.gov/sshws.shtml, accessed July 2010

[114] Wolf, G., "Let the Rebuild Begin," *Transmission & Distribution World*, December 1, 2008, http://tdworld.com/overhead_transmission/let_rebuild_begin_1208/index2.html, accessed May 22, 2010.
[115] Institute of Electrical and Electronics Engineers (IEEE), National Electrical Safety Codes (NESC), August 2006, http://standards.ieee.org/nesc/, accessed June 26, 2010.
[116] LPSC Docket Search Page. Docket No. R-30820. https://p8.lpsc.org/Workplace/Search.jsp, accessed June 10, 2010.
[117] PUCT. Project NO 32182. "PUC Investigation of Methods to Improve Electric and Telecommunications Infrastructure to Minimize Long Term Outages and Restoration Costs Associated with Gulf Coast Hurricanes." Final Staff Report. August 11, 2006. http://www.puc.state.tx.us/electric/reports/32182/32182.pdf, accessed June 10, 2010.
[118] Florida PSC, "Report to the Legislature on Enhancing the Reliability of Florida's Distribution and Transmission Grids During Extreme Weather (Update to July 2007 Report)," July 2008, http://www.floridapsc.com/utilities/electricgas/eiproject/, accessed June 10, 2010.
[119] TECO Distribution Reliability Report 2008. http://www.psc.state.fl.us/utilities/electricgas/docs/2008DistributionReliabilityReport.pdf, accessed June 10, 2010.
[120] Gulf Power Distribution Reliability Report 2008, p.21. http://www.psc.state electricgas/docs/2008DistributionReliabilityReport.pdf, accessed June 10, 2010.
[121] FPUC Distribution Reliability Report 2008. http://www.psc.stateelectricgas/docs/2008DistributionReliabilityReport.pdf, accessed June 10, 2010.
[122] SCE&G, http://www.sceg.com/NR/rdonlyres/465E6534-2FFB-4069-BF84-81465AEEF887/0/%20Undergroundvs.pdf, accessed May 14, 2010.
[123] Progress Energy Storm Hardening Plan, May 7, 2007, http://www.psc.state electricgas/docs/2008DistributionReliabilityReport.pdf, accessed June 10, 2010.
[124] Rollins, M., "The Hardening of Utility Lines – Implications for Utility pole Design and Use," presented at Utility Pole Conference & Trade Show, October 10, 2007, Vancouver, WA, http://www.woodpoles.org/documents/TheHardeningofUtilityLines.doc, accessed June 10, 2010.
[125] LPSC Docket Search Page. Docket No. R-30820. https://p8.lpsc.org/Workplace/Search.jsp, accessed June 10, 2010.
[126] USDA, http://www.usda.gov/rus/electric/pubs/1724e300/1724e300.pdf, accessed May 14, 2010.
[127] NIST, *Performance of Physical Structures in Hurricane Katrina and Hurricane Rita: A Reconnaissance Report*, NIST Technical Note 1476, June 2006, http://www.bfrl.nist.gov/investigations/pubs/NIST_TN_1476.pdf, accessed April 22, 2010.
[128] LPSC Docket No. U-31075, January 27, 2010, https://p8.lpsc.org/Workplace/Search.jsp, and "SLEMCO Engineers a New Approach to Protect Erath's Substation," *SLEMCO Power* Jan-Feb 2010, http://www.slemco.com/pdf_folder/magpdfs110/JF10PG7.PDF, accessed June 10, 2010.
[129] PUCT, Project No 32182, "PUC Investigation of Methods to Improve Electric and Telecommunications Infrastructure to Minimize Long Term Outages and Restoration Costs Associated with Gulf Coast Hurricanes," Final Staff Report, August 11, 2006, http://www.puc.state.tx.us/electric/reports/32182/32182.pdf, accessed June 10, 2010.
[130] NOAA/NHC, Hurricane Preparedness, SLOSH Model, http://www.nhc.noaa.gov/HAW2/english/surge/slosh.shtml, accessed June 10, 2010.
[131] FPUC Distribution Reliability Report 2008, http://www.psc.state.fl.us/utilities/electricgas/docs/2008DistributionReliabilityReport.pdf, accessed June 10, 2010. Reclosers are protective devices that interrupt the current when a fault is sensed.
[132] "Mississippi Power moves critical functions to safer location," News Release, May 22, 2007, http://pressroom-publisher.southerncompany.com/mpc/mpc21.html, accessed May 22, 2010.

[133] Davis, C. and B. Holley, "Shelter from the Storms," *Transmission & Distribution World*, Sep 1, 2008, http://tdworld.com/overhead_distribution/shelter_storms_alabama/index.html, accessed May 22, 2010.

[134] Northway, Wally, "New Entergy complex designed to 'better meet' commitments," Mississippi Business Journal, Nov 19, 2007, http://findarticles.com/p/articles/mi_qa5277/is_200711/ai_n21274289/, accessed April 22, 2010.

[135] Mc Culla, M. and Cassingham, P, "LightsOn: AFTER THE STORM," *Electric Energy Online*.htm, April 22, 2010, http://www.electricenergyonline.com/?page=show_article&mag=&article=488, accessed May 4, 2010.

[136] DeMarco, C., "Trends in Electrical Transmission and Distribution Technology, PSERC, February 2006, http://www.mrec.org/pubs/06%20MREC%20DeMarco%20PSERC.pdf, p. 12, accessed June 28, 2010.

[137] Managing Aged Transformers," *Transmission & Distribution World*, July 1, 2005, http://tdworld.com/substations/power_managing_aged_transformers/, accessed June 28, 2010.

[138] Edison Electric Institute, "Transmission Projects: At A Glance," February 2010, http://www.eei.org/OURISSUES/ELECTRICITYTRANSMISSION/Pages/TransmissionProjectsAt.aspx, accessed July 1, 2010.

[139] A Brief History of Electric Utility Automation Systems, *Electric Energy Online* http://www.electricenergyonline.com/?page=show_article&mag=63&article=491, accessed June 10, 2010.

[140] Meehan, B., "Enterprise GIS and the Smart Electric Grid," ESRI, http://www.esri.com/library/articles/enterprise- seg.pdf, accessed July 1, 2010.

[141] Broadband and Wireless Networking Laboratory, Substation Automation, http://www.ece.gatech.edu/research/labs/bwn/substation/, accessed June 10, 2010.

[142] FedSoft, WHAT IS AM/FM? Automated Mapping and Facilities Management, http://www.fedsoft.net/automatedmapping.htm#OVERVIEW, accessed June 27, 2010.

[143] Entergy, Entergy Texas Ready for 2006 Hurricane Season, http://www-temp.entergy.com/News_Room/newsrelease.aspx?NR_ID=842, accessed June 27, 2010.

[144] ESRI, Utility Praised for Quick Response, Restoration after Hurricane Ike, press release, August 3, 2009, http://www.esri.com/news/releases/09_3qtr/hurricane.html, accessed June 27, 2010.

[145] North American SynchroPhasor Initiative, http://www.naspi.org/, accessed May 17, 2010.

[146] PUCT Rulemaking, Project 37475, http://www.puc.state.tx.us/rules/rulemake/37475/37475adt.pdf, accessed July 1, 2010.

[147] Florida PSC, Report to the Legislature on Enhancing the Reliability of Florida's Distribution and Transmission Grids During Extreme Weather (Update to July 2007 Report), July 2008, http://www.floridapsc.com/utilities/electricgas/eiproject/docs/AddendumSHLegislature.pdf, accessed June 10, 2010.

[148] PUCT, PUC Investigation of Methods to Improve Electric and Telecom Infrastructure that will Minimize Long Term Outages and Restoration Costs Associated with Gulf Coast Hurricanes: Initial Comments of CenterPoint Energy Houston Electric, LLC, January 17,2006. http://interchange.puc.state.tx.us/WebApp/Interchange/Documents/32182_7_500961.PDF, accessed June 10, 2010.

[149] ThermoVision Infrared, Scanning Service: Prevent electrical system failures before they happen, http://www.les.com/pdf/ThermoVision.pdf, accessed April 12, 2010.

[150] LPSC Docket Search Page, Docket No. R-30820, https://p8.lpsc.org/Workplace/Search.jsp, accessed June 10, 2010.

[151] FERC Study. Utility Vegetation Management, http://www.ferc.gov/industries/electric/indus-act/reliability/blackout/uvm-final-report.pdf, accessed July 1, 2010.

[152] North American Electric Reliability Corporation, Standard FAC-003-1 — Transmission Vegetation Management Program, http://www.nerc.com/files/FAC-003-1.pdf, accessed June 28, 2010.

[153] Florida PSC, Order No. PSC-06-0351-PAA-EI, April 25, 2006. http://www.psc.state library/filings/06%5C03645-06%5C03645-06.PDF, accessed June 10, 2010.

[154] FPUC Distribution Reliability Report 2008. Page 41. http://www.psc.state electricgas/docs/2008DistributionReliabilityReport.pdf, accessed June 10, 2010.

[155] Shaner, J., "Electric Sector Responses to Hurricanes RMAG Approach," NARUC Critical Infrastructure Committee, Feb. 11, 2009, http://www.narucmeetings.org/Presentations/2nd %20Allegheny%20Power%20John%20Shaner%20on%20Electric%20Sector%20Response %20and%20RMAGs.pdf, accessed June 12, 2010.

[156] Ball, B. "Rebuilding Electrical Infrastructure along the Gulf Coast: A Case Study." *The Bridge,* Vol 36, No. 1. National Academy of Engineering, March 2006, http://www.nae.edu/Publications/TheBridge/Archives/V-36- 1TheAftermathofKatrina/ RebuildingElectricalInfrastructurealongtheGulfCoastACaseStudy.aspx, accessed April 22, 2010.

[157] Wolf, G., "Let the Rebuild Begin," *Transmission & Distribution World*, December 1, 2008, http://tdworld.com/overhead_transmission/let_rebuild_begin_1208/index2.html, accessed May 22, 2010.

[158] DOE/OE, Benefits of Using Mobile Transformers and Mobile Substations For Rapidly Restoring Electrical Service. EPAct 1816, August 2006, http://www.oe.energy MTS_Report_to_Congress_FINAL_73106.pdf, accessed May 14, 2010.

[159] Mining, J. and Chapman, R., "Mobilized for Battle," *Transmission & Distribution World*, December 1, 2008, http://tdworld.com/overhead_distribution ?smte=wr, accessed May 4, 2010.

[160] Wolf, G., "Let the Rebuild Begin," *Transmission & Distribution World*, December 1, 2008, http://tdworld.com/overhead_transmission/let_rebuild_begin_1208/index2.html, accessed May 22, 2010.

[161] PUCT Project No 32182, "PUC Investigation of Methods to Improve Electric and Telecommunications Infrastructure to Minimize Long Term Outages and Restoration Costs Associated with Gulf Coast Hurricanes," Final Staff Report. August 11, 2006. http://www.puc.state.tx.us/electric/reports/32182/32182.pdf , accessed June 10, 2010.

[162] Wolf, G., "Let the Rebuild Begin." *Transmission & Distribution World*, December 1, 2008, http://tdworld.com/overhead_transmission/let_rebuild_begin_1208/index2.html, accessed May 22, 2010.

[163] Ball, B., "Rebuilding Electrical Infrastructure along the Gulf Coast: A Case Study." *The Bridge,* Vol 36, No. 1. National Academy of Engineering, March 2006, http://www.nae.edu/ Publications/TheBridge/Archives/V-36-1TheAftermathofKatrina/RebuildingElectrical InfrastructurealongtheGulfCoastACaseStudy.aspx, accessed April 22, 2010.

[164] *Ibid.*

[165] Ground Control Global Satellite Internet Solutions. "Katrina Case Study." http://www.ground control.com/katrina.htm, accessed June 28, 2010.

[166] Wolf, G., "Let the Rebuild Begin." *Transmission & Distribution World*, December 1, 2008, http://tdworld.com/overhead_transmission/let_rebuild_begin_1208/index2.html, accessed May 22, 2010.

[167] Mining, J. and Chapman, R., "Mobilized for Battle." *Transmission & Distribution World*, December 1, 2008, http://tdworld.com/overhead_distribution/mobilized_for_battle_1208/ ?smte=wr, accessed May 4, 2010.

[168] Ball, B., "Rebuilding Electrical Infrastructure along the Gulf Coast: A Case Study," *The Bridge,* Vol 36, No. 1, National Academy of Engineering, March 2006, http://www.nae.edu/Publications/TheBridge/Archives/V-36-1TheAftermathofKatrina/ RebuildingElectricalInfrastructurealongtheGulfCoastACaseStudy.aspx, accessed April 22, 2010.

[169] The Progressive Engineer, http://www.progressiveengineer.com/company_profiles/hesco.htm, accessed May 7, 2010.

[170] HESCO, http://www.hesco.com/US_CIVIL/floodline.html, accessed May 7, 2010.

[171]Construction International. HESCO Concertainer used in Hurricane Katrina Aftermath - New Orleans, Louisiana, http://www.construction hesco-concertainer-used-in-hurricane-katrina-aftermath-new-orleans-louisiana.asp, accessed May 7, 2010.

[172] ORNL, http://www.ornl.org/sci/eere/PDFs/sci_tech_hilights/2007_no2_st_highlights.pdf, accessed June 28, 2010.

[173] EPRI, Phasor Measurement Unit (PMU) Implementation and Applications. http://my.epri.com/portal/server.pt?Abstract_id=000000000001015511, accessed May 7, 2010.

[174] Alliance Composite, Inc., http://www.alliancecompositesinc.com/Site/Why_Composite_Poles.html, accessed May 7, 2010.

[175] Shakespeare Composite Structures, http://skp-cs.com/poleproducts/td/tdreport.asp#Climbing, accessed May 7, 2010.

[176] *Transmission & Distribution World*, http://tdworld.com/mag/power_frp_composite_poles/, accessed May 7,

[177] ThermoVision Infrared, Scanning Service: Prevent electrical system failures before they happen, http://www.les.com/pdf/ThermoVision.pdf, accessed June 27, 2010.

[178] Kregg, M., ComEd Energy Delivery, Power Quality Department, Development of a Utility Feeder Infrared Thermography Preventive Maintenance Program, http://www.utilityscanir.com/papers/Dev_Utility_Feeder1.pdf, accessed June 27, 2010.

[179] ORNL, "ORNL wins six R&D 100 Awards, pushing total to 134," July 2, 2007 press release, http://www.ornl.gov/info/press_releases/get_press_release.cfm?ReleaseNumber=mr20070702-00, accessed June 27, 2010.

[180] Osmose Utility Services, Inc., ET-Truss: Pole Strengthening System, http://www.osmoseutilities.com/content/pages/et-truss, accessed June 28, 2010.

[181] CenterPoint Energy, http://www.centerpointenergy.com/services/electricity/ competitive retailers/smartmeters/news/13ddb2f7e2c87210VgnVCM10000026a10d0aRCRD/, accessed May 7, 2010.

[182] "Electrical Equipment – Winners: Recloser minimizes power interruptions," *R&D Magazine*, July 28, 2009, http://www.rdmag.com/Awards-Winners.aspx?id=632, accessed May 4, 2010.

In: U.S. Energy Industry Response ...
Editor: Ilya Bertolucci
ISBN: 978-1-62808-944-8

Chapter 2

COMPARING THE IMPACTS OF THE 2005 AND 2008 HURRICANES ON U.S. ENERGY INFRASTRUCTURE*

U.S. Department of Energy

EXECUTIVE SUMMARY

Hurricanes Gustav and Ike struck the U.S. Gulf within two weeks of each other in September 2008, severely damaging energy infrastructure and disrupting oil and gas supplies throughout the United States. Millions of electricity customers lost power as the storms knocked down thousands of miles of transmission and distribution lines, and forced shut hundreds of substations. Two nuclear power plants were shut due to the storm. Extended electricity outages delayed the restoration of refineries, pipelines, gas processors, and other energy facilities that depend on grid-delivered power.

Oil and gas platform operators shuttered offshore production in the Gulf of Mexico as a precaution before both storms and damage caused by the storms kept a significant portion of that production offline several months after the storms passed. Some smaller platforms were completely destroyed and a small amount of Gulf of Mexico oil and gas production is likely to be permanently lost. Hurricanes Gustav and Ike also shut onshore natural gas

* This report was prepared by the Office of Electricity Delivery and Energy Reliability on February 2009.

processing plants and several gas pipelines, restricting the flow of gas throughout the United States for weeks. Despite the supply curtailment, natural gas prices remained stable both before and after the storms made landfall.

U.S. petroleum supply was also impacted by the hurricanes, which shut key petroleum infrastructure, including refineries, ports, waterways, and pipelines. More than a dozen refineries were shut as a precaution before each hurricane, but only a few remained offline for several weeks after Hurricane Ike due to lack of power supply. Port closures disrupted crude oil and petroleum product imports into the Gulf and once ports reopened, product imports were limited by stringent quality standards for gasoline and distillate fuel. Although stocks of petroleum products were sufficient in the Gulf, the closure of key product pipelines, ports, and waterways prevented many of these supplies from reaching consumer markets. Fuel supply problems were particularly acute in the Southeast, which is highly dependent on supply from two key petroleum products pipelines fed by Gulf refineries. A combination of supply shortages and panic buying occurred in the Southeast in the weeks following Gustav and Ike. Spot gasoline and diesel prices briefly spiked as Hurricane Ike approached and the market anticipated serious damage to Texas refineries but quickly returned to pre-storm levels after site assessments revealed only minor damage.

Table ES-1. Energy Impacts of 2005 Hurricanes vs. 2008 Hurricanes

Energy Type Impacted	2005			2008	
	Katrina 8/30/05	Rita 9/25/05	Wilma 10/25/05	Gustav 9/2/08	Ike 9/14/08
Electricity (Million Customers)	2.7	1.5	3.5	1.1	3.9
Natural Gas Production (Bcf/d)	8.8	8.1	0	7.1	7.3
Oil Production (MMBD)	1.4	1.5	0	1.3	1.3

Notes: Bcf/d = billion cubic feet per day; MMBD = million barrels per day. Sources: OE/ISER Situation Reports, MMS.

The energy infrastructure and supply disruptions caused by the 2008 hurricanes were similar but not as severe as those caused by Hurricanes Katrina, Rita and Wilma in 2005 (See Table ES-1.) Although worst-day outages between both hurricane seasons were comparable, Hurricanes Katrina and Rita were more powerful and caused more lasting damage to energy infrastructure than Hurricanes Gustav and Ike. As a result, energy production and supply recovered more quickly in 2008 than in 2005.

Recovery in 2008 was hastened by the actions of the energy industry and Federal, State, and local government agencies, which were better prepared to mount extensive restoration efforts after the experience gained from 2005. Many Federal agencies helped with energy restoration, including the Department of Energy (DOE). The DOE Office of Electricity Delivery and Energy Reliability, Infrastructure Security and Energy Restoration division (OE/ISER) helped facilitate the restoration of damaged energy systems and components through a variety of actions. OE ISER sent its Emergency Support Function #12 (ESF-12) responders to field offices in the Gulf to work with other Federal, State, and local officials and industry representatives to identify damaged infrastructure, prioritize restoration efforts, and recommend emergency actions. OE/ISER monitored and reported on damage assessment, restoration efforts and recovery estimates, and supported decision making by other government agencies responsible for granting waivers to help alleviate energy supply problems. DOE released crude oil from its Strategic Petroleum Reserve at the request of refiners experiencing supply problems in the wake of the hurricanes and monitored fuel prices to make certain that consumers were paying appropriate prices at the pump.

This report compares the impact of the major hurricanes of 2005 and 2008 on U.S. energy systems, including those that produce, process and transport oil, natural gas, and electricity. The magnitude and duration of hurricane-induced production and supply disruptions are compared, as well as the extent of damage to energy infrastructure. The effect of disruptions on energy prices and supply is analyzed. The report describes the actions taken by DOE and other Federal agencies to assist the energy industry in restoration.

The primary sources of 2005 and 2008 data provided in this report are the Emergency Situation Reports prepared by OE/ISER and available on the public web site, http://www.oe.netl.doe.gov/emergency sit rpt.aspx. The Energy Assurance Daily during the periods under study is used to provide supporting details and can be found at http://www.oe.netl.doe.gov/ead.aspx. Footnotes are provided where other sources are used in the report.

STORM PATHS

The 2005 Atlantic hurricane season was the most active in recorded history, setting records for the number of named storms, the number of hurricanes, and the costliest hurricane (see Table 1). Of the storms that made

U.S. landfall, three of the season's seven major hurricanes—Katrina, Rita, and Wilma—were responsible for most of the destruction.

Table 1. Seasonal Records of 2005 and 2008 Hurricanes

Seasonal Records[1]	2005	2008
Named storms	#1 – 27 named storms	#7 – 16 named storms
Hurricanes	#1 – 15 hurricanes	#25 – 8 hurricanes
Major hurricanes[2]	#1 – 7 major hurricanes (4 reached Category 5 status)	#9 – 5 major hurricanes
Longest seasons[3]	#2 – 126.5 days	#13 – 84.75 days
Costliest hurricanes	#1 – Katrina $100 + billion	#4 – Ike $16.2 billion
Deadliest hurricanes	#3 – Katrina 1,000 + dead	#26 – Ike 82 dead
Focus on 5 Storms Category, State, Date at Landfall	Katrina Cat. 1 FL8/25/05 Cat 3 LA8/29/05	Gustav Cat 2 LA 9/1/08
	Rita Cat 3 TX/LA 9/24/05	Ike Cat 2 TX9/13/08

Sources: http://www.noaanews.noaa.gov/stories2008/20081126_hurricaneseason.html; http://www.ncdc.noaa.gov/oa/climate/research/2005/hurricanes05.html; http://www.nhc.noaa.gov/HAW2/english/history.shtml; http://www.nhc.noaa.gov/ms-word/TCRAL122005_Katrina.doc; http://www.nhc.noaa.gov/archive/2008/tws/MIATWSAT_nov.shtml; http://www.wunderground.com/blog/JeffMasters/archive.html?year=2008&month=11; http://www.wunderground.com/blog/JeffMasters/comment.html?entrynum=252&tstamp=200512.

Notes:

[1] Since 1900, according to the National Hurricane Center.

[2] Category 3 or higher.

[3] Number of named storm days in each year.

The most catastrophic effects of the season were felt on the U.S. Gulf Coast, where a 30-foot storm surge from Hurricane Katrina on August 29, 2005, caused devastating flooding that inundated New Orleans, Louisiana, and destroyed most structures on the Mississippi coastline. One month later, Hurricane Rita caused renewed flooding in New Orleans before making landfall on the Texas-Louisiana border, flooding the cities of Beaumont and Port Arthur, Texas. Hurricanes Dennis and Wilma both made landfall in Florida while Ophelia skirted the coast of North Carolina.

The 2008 Atlantic hurricane season was one of the most active on record but was not as severe as the 2005 season. Within a two-month period in 2008, three hurricanes and two tropical storms made landfall in the United States[1].

2 hurricane – 1 mph below Category 3 level. Gustav made landfall to the west of where Hurricane Katrina hit in 2005, tearing through south central Louisiana and bringing significant flooding as far north as Baton Rouge. Hurricane Ike made landfall 13 days later as a Category 2 Hurricane. Ike, which made landfall at Galveston, Texas, to the west of where Rita made landfall as a Category 3 Hurricane in 2005, caused significant damage in the Houston area before racing across the eastern United States, impacting the Midwest and communities as far north as New York.

Of all the storms that made landfall in 2005 and 2008, this analysis is focused on Katrina, Rita, and Wilma (for electricity impacts only) in 2005 and Gustav and Ike in 2008. Figure 1 shows the paths of the three most powerful hurricanes in 2005 – Katrina (purple), Rita (orange), and Wilma (brown). The two most damaging hurricanes of 2008 – Gustav (green) and Ike (blue) – are layered on top to show the common paths.

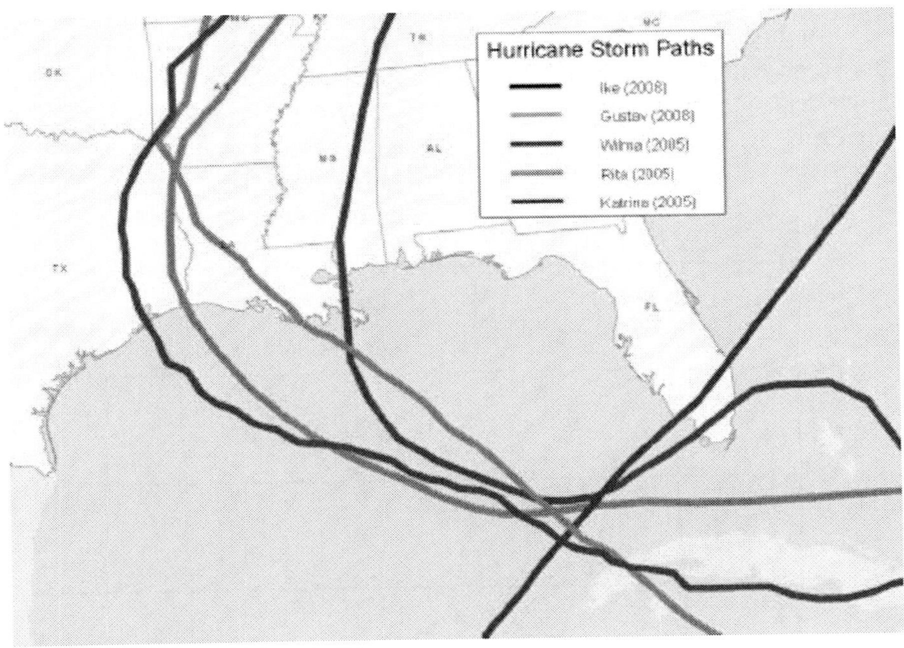

Source: NOAA.

Figure 1. Paths of Major Hurricanes in 2005 and 2008.

Both the 2005 and 2008 hurricane seasons caused severe damage and had lasting impacts on all types of energy infrastructure. However, the 2005 hurricane season was considerably more active in terms of the number of named storms, the number of storms that became hurricanes, and the intensity of the storms upon landfall.

In 2008, a weaker hurricane season coupled with better preparations by the oil, gas and electricity industries resulted in less severe impacts on energy infrastructure than in 2005.

ELECTRICITY

Customer Outages

The hurricanes and tropical storms of 2005 and 2008 caused major power outages as high winds and heavy rains resulted in significant damage to electricity transmission and distribution networks.

The magnitude of the power outages was determined by the intensity of the storm and the population density of the communities in the storm path. High density coastal communities with above ground power lines were most affected.

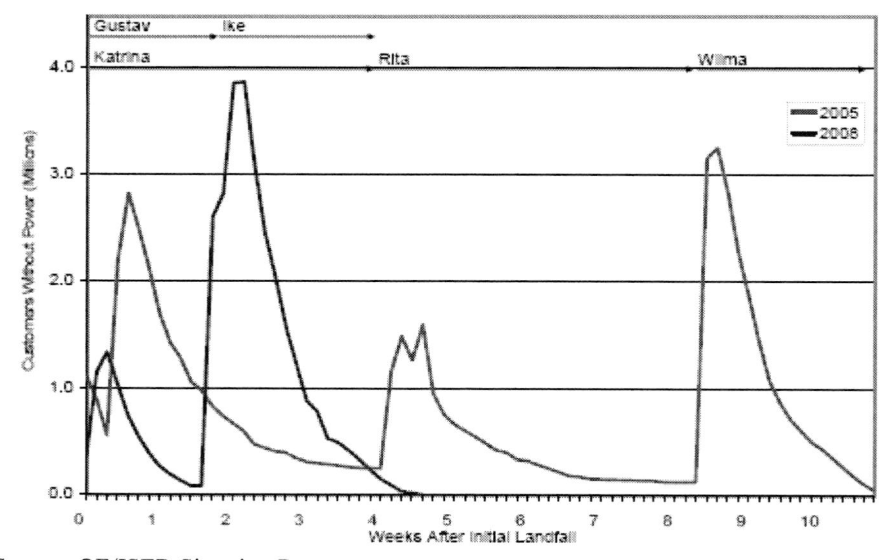

Source: OE/ISER Situation Reports.

Figure 2. Electricity Customer Outages from 2005 and 2008 Hurricanes.

In 2005, three major hurricanes made direct hits in the heavily populated areas of Miami, New Orleans, and Houston, impacting electricity assets owned and operated by Florida Power & Light, CenterPoint Energy, three Entergy operating companies (New Orleans, Gulf States, and Louisiana), and several other utilities operating in the Gulf.

Electricity customer outages caused by Hurricane Katrina were greater in magnitude and duration than those caused by Hurricane Rita (see Figure 2 and State outages in Appendix Table A-1). Hurricane Katrina knocked out power to more than 1 million customers in Florida before crossing the Gulf of Mexico and making a second landfall in Louisiana. At its peak on August 30, 2005, an estimated 2.7 million customers were without power across four states. Two weeks after Katrina first made landfall in the United States, power had been fully restored to customers in Alabama, Florida, and Mississippi, yet over 40 percent of the customers in the state of Louisiana remained without power.

The storm blacked out the city of New Orleans (see Figure 3). Restoration efforts were complicated by extensive flooding, particularly in the areas of New Orleans that were submerged when the levees on Lake Pontchartrain were breached. As a result, Entergy New Orleans was unable to fully restore power for several months. The investor-owned utility (IOU), facing estimated restoration costs in the range of $260 to $325 million and a loss of customer revenue estimated at $147 million, filed for bankruptcy in late September 2005.[2] The utility did not emerge from Chapter 11 bankruptcy until May 2007.[3]

Hurricane Rita, which made landfall along the Texas-Louisiana border on September 24, 2005, less than one month after Katrina, knocked out power to more than 1.3 million customers at its peak, bringing total customers without power from both storms to nearly 1.6 million. New outages from Rita were restored in less than three weeks. On October 21, 2005, eight weeks after Katrina first made landfall in Florida, all but 120,000 customers had been restored from hurricanes Katrina and Rita. The remaining outages were customers of Entergy New Orleans whose residences were too damaged by Hurricane Katrina to permit electric service restoration.

The third storm of significance in 2005 was Hurricane Wilma, which was the 13th hurricane of the season. Wilma made landfall in Florida as a Category 3 hurricane, knocking out power to 3.5 million customers in the population-dense communities of southern Florida on October 24, 2005. Hurricane force winds cut a 180-mile swath across the state, blacking out 60 percent of Florida Power & Light's 35-county territory.

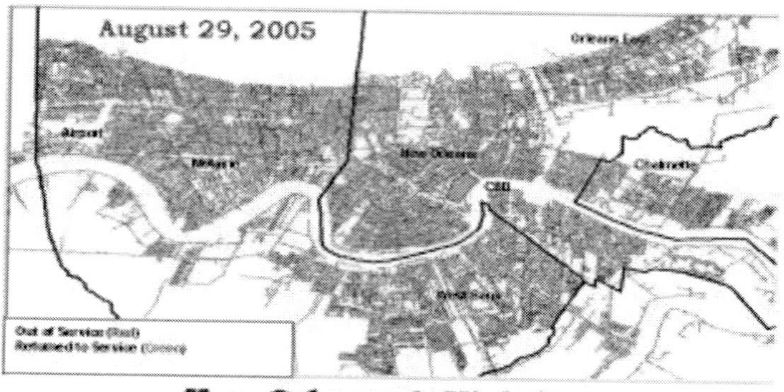

New Orleans & Vicinity

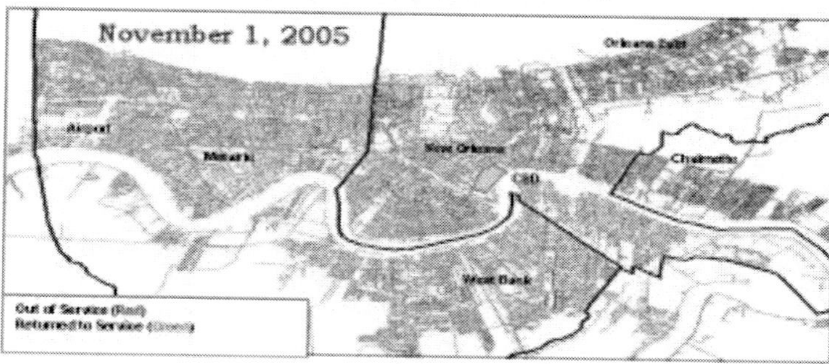

Source: Entergy.

Figure 3. Entergy New Orleans Customer Outage Progression, 2005.

In Miami-Dade County, 98 percent of the IOU's customers, including major airports, hospitals, and Port Everglades lost power. Restoration proceeded quickly with the help of 18,000 workers from 33 states and Canada and two weeks after Hurricane Wilma made landfall, only 100,000 customers remained without power (see Appendix Table A-2).

Power outages caused by Hurricanes Gustav and Ike in 2008 were comparable in magnitude but shorter in duration than those caused by Katrina and Rita in 2005. Hurricane Gustav's outages, which peaked at more than 1.3 million customers on September 2, 2008, were concentrated primarily in Louisiana, Mississippi, and Arkansas. Gustav caused severe flooding in Baton Rouge, Louisiana, and raised water levels on the Mississippi River, shutting down locks and impacting waterborne deliveries of fuel to power plants and plant access to the river for cooling. The floods slowed the restoration efforts of Entergy and thousands of out of state workers who arrived to help restore power.

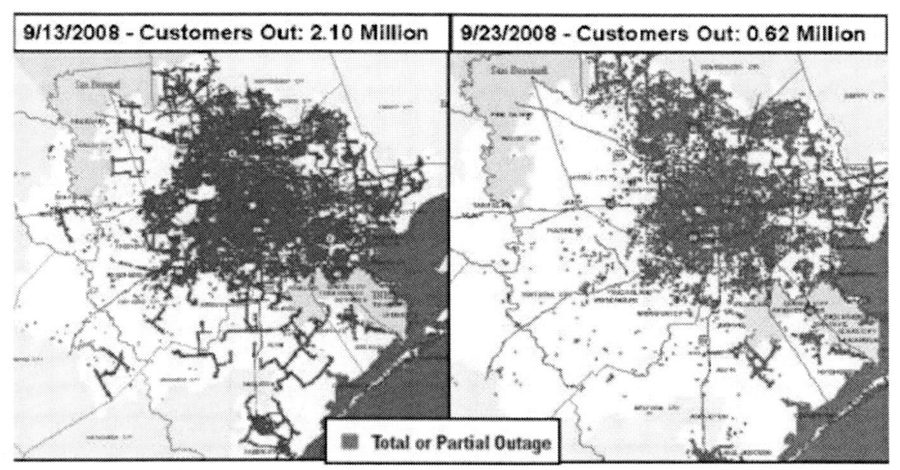

Source: CenterPoint Energy.

Figure 4. CenterPoint Energy (Houston) Customer Outage Progression, September 2008.

Power outages from Hurricane Ike, which made landfall on September 13, 2008, less than two weeks after Gustav, were greater in magnitude and covered a greater geographic region than Gustav. Ike ripped through major population centers in Galveston, Houston, and Port Arthur, Texas, knocking out power to virtually all customers in the service territories served by CenterPoint Energy and Entergy Texas. The hurricane continued to move northward, knocking out power to customers in Arkansas, Louisiana, Missouri, Kentucky, Indiana, Ohio, and New York. As reported in the Situation Report on September 14, 2008, Ike had blacked out a total of 3.9 million customers across nine states,[4] making it the largest North American power outage since the great Northeast blackout of August 14, 2003. More than half of these outages affected customers in CenterPoint Energy's Houston metropolitan service territory and much of the city remained without power for more than ten days after Ike struck(see Figure 4).

Transmission & Distribution

The prime cause of electricity outages during both the 2005 and 2008 hurricanes was damage to the electricity transmission and distribution systems along the Gulf Coast (see Table 2). The number of poles destroyed exceeded

72,000 for Hurricane Katrina. Both wooden and steel structures were damaged and key transmission lines were out of service for weeks. Entergy New Orleans did not report the number of poles destroyed, and as a result infrastructure impacts from Katrina are underestimated. Electric cooperatives in Mississippi reported that more than 50,000 utility distribution poles were destroyed by Hurricane Katrina. One Louisiana cooperative indicated that an estimated 3,500 miles of its power lines and poles were blown to the ground.[5]

Table 2. U.S. Gulf Electric Infrastructure Impacted by Hurricanes, 2005 vs. 2008

Infrastructure Impacted	2005			2008	
	Katrina	Rita	Wilma	Gustav	Ike
Utility Poles Destroyed	72,447	14,817	~14,000	11,478	10,300
Transformers Damaged	8,281	3,580	NA	4,349	2,900
Transmission Structures Damaged	1,515	3,550	NA	241	238
Substations Off-line	300	508	241	368	383

Sources: ISER Situation Reports from 2005 and 2008; Entergy, CLECO, and Sam Houston news releases; SLEMCO Power.

Based on damage to transmission and distribution structures reported by Entergy Louisiana, Entergy Gulf States, Centerpoint Energy, CLECO, Mississippi Power, Florida Power & Light, Sam Houston Electric Coop (Texas) and Mississippi cooperatives. Data is not comprehensive; excludes comparable data from Entergy New Orleans, and all cooperatives and municipal energy utilities throughout the Gulf.

Twice as many miles of lines were downed by Hurricane Katrina than Hurricane Rita. However, Rita had a greater impact on substations – taking over 500 off-line. Entergy's bulk transmission in east Texas sustained severe damage from Hurricane Rita, including 500-kV lines with damaged structures. Hurricane Wilma damaged more poles than the sum of those replaced after the 2004 Hurricanes Charley, Frances and Jeanne.

The damage to the Entergy system from Hurricane Gustav was the worst ever in the Baton Rouge area. Gustav also impacted the electricity grid in southeastern Louisiana. Due to damage to several high-voltage transmission lines, a portion of Entergy's transmission system south of Lake Pontchartrain, including the city of New Orleans, was "islanded," meaning that the system was disconnected from the rest of the Entergy supply network. The islanded grid was reconnected to the Entergy system after two days by restoring East-

West transmission line connections.[6] In areas where the damage was the most extensive or where access was the most difficult, it took several weeks before necessary repairs were completed.

Hurricane Ike shut down over 30 transmission circuits and almost 1,000 distribution circuits in CenterPoint Energy's service territory in Texas. Thousands of mutual assistance linemen from 31 states and Canada came to help the restoration efforts in Texas. In less than three weeks, Centerpoint reported it had restored electricity to all customers who could receive power in Texas.

Power Plants

The power outages experienced during the 2005 and 2008 hurricanes were not due to power plant closings. Nuclear power plant maintenance and refueling proceeded as scheduled during both hurricane seasons, according to the Nuclear Regulatory Commission.

Three nuclear power plants lay within the area affected by Hurricane Katrina but none of the plants experienced any significant damage or flooding (see Table 3). Only one of the plants, the Waterford plant near New Orleans, shut in advance of Hurricane Katrina and remained shut for two weeks before restarting. The other two plants, River Bend and Grand Gulf, continued to produce electricity during and after the storm but operated at reduced capacity because of reduced electricity demand or damage to electricity delivery infrastructure that prevented integration of full output from the plants.[7] No nuclear power plants were shut by the arrival of either Hurricane Rita or Wilma.

Table 3. Nuclear Power Plants Affected by Hurricanes, 2005 and 2008

Year	Unit	State	Company	Capacity (MW)	Impact Start Impact Date	Restoration Date*
2005	Waterford 3	LA	Entergy	1,075	Shut Down 8/29/05	9/16/05
	River Bend 1	LA	Entergy	966	Reduced 8/30/05	9/5/05
	Grand Gulf 1	MS	Entergy	1,207	Reduced 8/30/05	9/6/05
2008	Waterford 3	LA	Entergy	1,075	Shut Down 8/31/08	9/12/08
	River Bend 1	LA	Entergy	966	Shut Down 9/2/08	9/29/08

Note: *Date of restoration to full capacity; not the same as restart date. Source: Nuclear Regulatory Commission.

In anticipation of Hurricane Gustav, Entergy performed a controlled shut down of its Waterford 3 nuclear plant on August 31, 2008. Waterford 3 returned to full service within two weeks. Entergy also shut its River Bend nuclear plant for four weeks when it suffered exterior building damage from Hurricane Gustav's winds. No nuclear plants were shut by Hurricane Ike.

Energy infrastructure is highly interdependent. Electricity outages from hurricanes resulted in the closing of refineries, gas processors, pipelines, ports, and other facilities in both 2005 and 2008. Prolonged electricity outages delayed the restoration efforts at these facilities.

NATURAL GAS

Production

The hurricanes of 2005 and 2008 disrupted many facilities that extract, process, and transport natural gas. In 2005, the Minerals Management Service (MMS) estimated that 3,050 of the 4,000 platforms and 22,000 of the 33,000 miles of gathering pipelines in the Gulf of Mexico were in the direct path of either Hurricane Katrina or Rita.[8] Before the 2005 hurricane season began, the offshore platforms in the Gulf of Mexico (Outer Continental Shelf, OCS) produced 10 billion cubic feet of gas per day (Bcf/d), or 20 percent of the natural gas produced in the United States. As Hurricane Katrina approached the Gulf in late August 2005, MMS reported that manned platforms and rigs in the potential storm path had been evacuated and 8.8 Bcf/d, or 88 percent of total Gulf production, was shut down as a precaution (see Figure 5 and Table A-3).

After Katrina passed, undamaged Gulf production facilities were quickly returned to service and one week after the storm hit, shut-in OCS production was reduced to about 4.0 Bcf/d.

Restoration at heavily damaged production facilities progressed more slowly and by September 20, 2005, shut-in production had been reduced to 3.4 Bcf/d before the approach of Hurricane Rita forced Gulf operators to again evacuate platforms and shut down production. As Rita approached, Gulf operators shut in an additional 4.7 Bcf/d as a precaution, bringing total offline Gulf production to 8.1 Bcf/d. Hurricane Rita, which veered farther west than Katrina, damaged many of the offshore facilities that had survived the passage of Katrina.

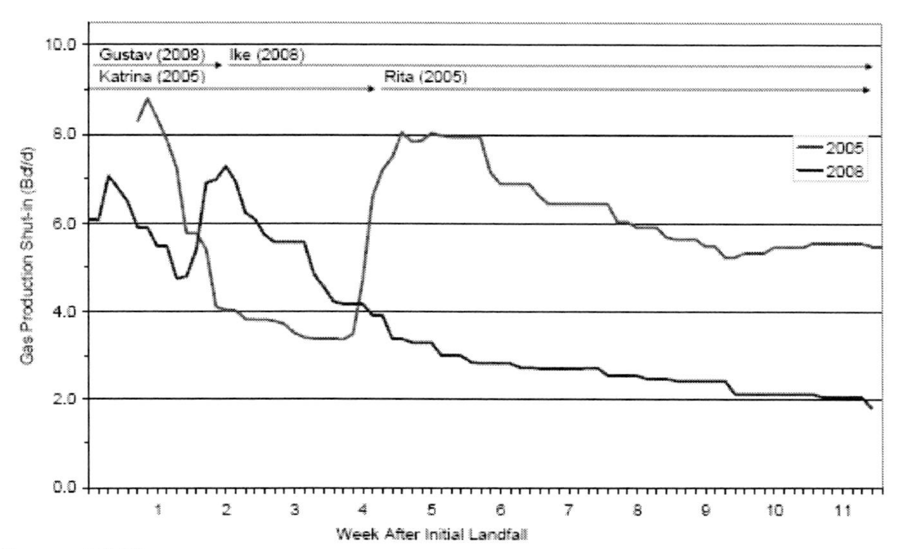

Source: MMS.

Note: MMS data collection began August 29, 2005, days after Katrina made landfall in Florida, moving across the Gulf.S MMS.

Figure 5. Gulf of Mexico OCS Natural Gas Production Shut In by 2005 and 2008 Hurricanes.

About 8.0 Bcf/d of Gulf production remained shut in for one week after Rita and restoration proceeded slowly thereafter, with 5.6 Bcf/d of gas production still shut-in four weeks after Rita made landfall. Restoration proceeded slowly from November 2005 through March 2006, when DOE discontinued its active monitoring of restoration efforts.

In addition to the MMS-monitored production fields in the Gulf of Mexico OCS, Hurricane Katrina and Rita also disrupted Gulf offshore gas production within three miles of the Louisiana coastline. This production is monitored by the Louisiana Department of Natural Resources (DNR).[9] At the start of the 2005 hurricane season, Louisiana offshore gas production averaged 2.2 Bcf/d. All of this production was shut down following Hurricanes Katrina and Rita. By December 27, 2005, three months after the passage of Rita, more than 0.6 Bcf/d remained shutin.[10] Most of this production was from smaller wells that operators deemed too small to restore and was lost permanently.

Restoration to Gulf OCS and Louisiana offshore facilities was slow due to the magnitude of the damage caused by the hurricanes (see Table 4). Industry assessments, investigations, and reports revealed a total of 457 pipelines damaged from the 2005 hurricanes. The number of larger diameter pipelines (10 inches or greater) that were damaged was 101.[11] Many of these pipelines were breached and large volumes of sea water had to be moved through the pipelines to shore where the lines could be dewatered and contaminants removed before returning to service.

Table 4. Natural Gas Operating Capacity in the Gulf of Mexico, 2005 and 2008

Source	2005 Capacity (Bcf/d)			2008 Capacity (Bcf/d)		
	Pre-Season	Season Low	Year-End	Pre-Season	Season Low	Year-End
Federal OCS	10.0	1.2	4.4	7.4	0.1	6.3
Louisiana DNR	2.2	0	1.6	1.6	0.3	1.1

Note: *Date of restoration to full capacity; not the same as restart date.

Source: MMS and Louisiana DNR, as reported in ISER Situation reports in 2005 and 2008.

In addition, restoration was hindered by complications caused by the depth of the water where the platforms and pipelines were most damaged, the limited number of crews able to make repairs in deep water, rough seas, and long lead times for delivery of parts and materials. Devastation to the offshore and onshore service industry supporting Gulf natural gas production also slowed recovery. The 2005 hurricanes significantly disrupted the network of work boats, crews, divers, supplies, and equipment needed to assess the damage and perform repairs to platforms and pipelines. Furthermore, docks and fleets were destroyed, electric power was lost on a wide-scale basis, and transportation fuels were not available for the boats, helicopters, and ground transportation vital to the recovery.[12]

Hurricanes Gustav and Ike in 2008 did not disrupt offshore gas production on the same scale as Katrina and Rita in 2005, despite following similar paths. Due to lasting effects from the 2005 hurricanes, there were almost 200 fewer operating production platforms in the Gulf of Mexico in August 2008, and the resulting capacity of Gulf of Mexico OCS production was reduced by more than 25 percent to 7.4 Bcf/d.

MMS estimated that approximately 2,127 of the 3,800 platforms in the Gulf of Mexico OCS were exposed to hurricane conditions in 2008, with winds greater than 74 miles per hour, from Hurricanes Gustav and Ike.[13] As Gustav approached, operators evacuated offshore platforms and began shutting in offshore gas production in the path of the storm. On September 2, 2008, one day after Gustav made landfall in Louisiana, more than 95 percent of Gulf gas production was shut–in. After the passage of Gustav, operators quickly restored production from some undamaged facilities but were forced to shut production again due to the rapid approach of Hurricane Ike, which cut through the Gulf making landfall less than two weeks later. After Ike, operators completed flyovers and damage assessments of platforms in the hurricane path before bringing production back online. Recovery proceeded at a measured pace throughout the remainder of September, with 3.9 Bcf/d, or more than 50 percent of total Gulf gas production, remaining shut-in by the end of the month. By February 11, 2009, only 0.9 Bcf/d or 13 percent of total OCS natural gas production remained shut-in. MMS estimates that 60 platforms were destroyed in the Gulf that produced a total of 0.1 Bcf/d.[14]

Louisiana offshore production, which lost 27 percent of its 2.2 Bcf/d capacity, was recalibrated to 1.6 Bcf/d after the 2005 hurricanes. Hurricane Gustav pushed through the coastal Louisiana parishes, and by September 10, 2008, more than one week after Gustav's landfall, only 0.3 Bcf/d was known to be producing. By November 17, 2008, about one and half months after Gustav, wells were producing 1.1 Bcf/d, shut-in capacity was 0.3 Bcf/d and the status of 0.2 Bcf/d was unknown.[15]

In addition to damage to platforms and rigs, restoration of offshore Gulf of Mexico and offshore Louisiana gas production was hindered by damage to pipelines needed to bring offshore production to onshore processing facilities. Hurricane Ike generated towering waves that caused major impacts to eight gas transmission pipelines originating in the Gulf of Mexico. Nearly all the pipeline damage was caused by toppled platforms and in one case, a jack-up drilling rig. These shut-in pipelines, including TransCanada's Central Gulf, Panhandle Energy's Sea Robin, and Williams Transcontinental, stopped the flow of natural gas from connected platforms.[16]

Processing

Onshore gas processing facilities were impacted by hurricanes in both 2005 and 2008. In 2005, there were at least 47 major gas processors in the Gulf Coast, mainly located in Louisiana, Texas, Mississippi and Alabama. Major processors have capacities of 0.15 Bcf/d or greater. These plants remove water, contaminants, and liquid hydrocarbons in order to prepare almost 23 Bcf/d of dry gas for end use. There were also 17 fractionators in the Gulf, the largest being the Mont Belvieu complex in southeast Texas, near the

Louisiana border.[17] A complete series of data on the operations of gas processors following Hurricane Katrina was not collected by EIA. As a result, it is not known precisely how many of these facilities were impacted and operable capacity data is not included in Figure 6 prior to September 30. This data is included in Appendix Tables A-3 and A-4 where appropriate.

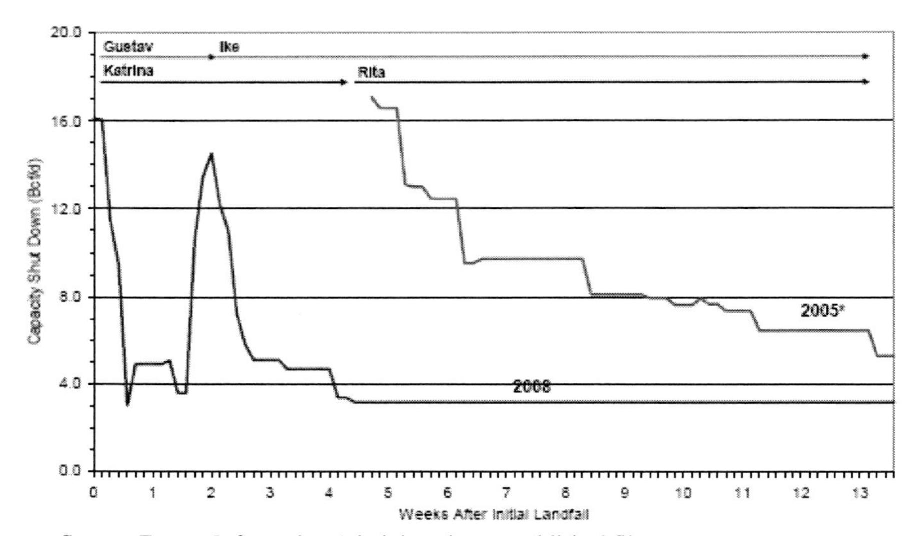

Source: Energy Information Administration, unpublished files.
Note: * EIA data unavailable prior to September 29, 2005.

Figure 6. Natural Gas Processors Shut Down by 2005 and 2008 Hurricanes.

Hurricane Katrina shut in at least eight major processors with a capacity of almost 7 Bcf/d. After Hurricane Rita made landfall, 27 natural gas processing plants, with a total capacity of 17 Bcf/d, were inactive in Texas, Louisiana, and Mississippi.

The majority of processing plants cited external factors as the reason for the 2005 plant closures. External factors include the lack of electric power experienced by many plants, lack of upstream supplies, inaccessibility to the plant because of road conditions, or lack of downstream capabilities.[18] At least one plant was permanently decommissioned in late January 2006 as a result of the damage received.

By 2008, EIA acquired more complete data on gas processors through a new survey.[19] A total of 97 gas processors in Texas, Louisiana, Mississippi and Alabama were in the region impacted by Hurricanes Gustav and/or Ike. Fifty-five of these 97 plants are major processors and represent 38 percent of the U.S.

productive capacity (including both lower 48 and Alaska).[20] Operators shut down 25 of these plants in advance of Hurricane Gustav, reducing gas production capacity by more than 16 Bcf/d. Some of these gas processors were flooded, lacked power, or suffered damage due to Gustav and were still shut down when Ike made landfall two weeks later. After Ike made landfall, a combined total of 30 processors in Texas and Louisiana were closed by both storms.

Several processors indicated that the unavailability of large fractionators, such as Mount Belvieu and Beaumont, and the shut-in of gathering pipelines from the Gulf of Mexico were the reasons for the processor outages. Restoration efforts were significant, with only five plants with 3.2 Bcf/d of capacity remaining shut down by the end of November 2008.[21]

Transportation

Natural gas pipeline companies operating in the U.S. Gulf, especially those moving gas from offshore production platforms to onshore processing plants, were impacted by Hurricanes Gustav and Ike in early September 2008. Twenty-eight pipelines declared *force majeure* or posted critical notices on their electronic bulletin boards.

This list is not comprehensive: these are the significant pipelines tracked by the ISER Situation Reports. Fourteen of these were gathering pipelines, that shut-in their systems because of damage to the pipelines or damage to the OCS production platforms.[22]

The other 14 were interstate longhaul pipelines also impacted by the restriction of gas supply from the Gulf.[23] They posted notices informing shippers of reduced supply from offshore production, shutdown of processing plants and compressor stations along their systems. Some pipeline compressor stations were operated on emergency backup generators as commercial electric power was unavailable for days.

Eleven major interstate pipelines had their flow significantly restricted on the worst days of both storms (see Appendix Table A-4). All of these interstate longhaul pipelines resumed normal or close to normal operations within four weeks after Ike made landfall, using stock withdrawls to keep their lines full.

The liquefied natural gas (LNG) import terminals located in the Gulf Coast were shut as a precaution in 2008, but none reported any major damage upon personnel returning to the facilities.

Stocks & Prices

Natural gas prices during the hurricane season were far more volatile in 2005 than 2008. Supply disruptions caused by Hurricanes Katrina and Rita led to large spikes in the spot prices for natural gas in both the Gulf (Henry Hub) and at the New York City gate. New York spot prices have always trended above Henry Hub spot prices, but the premium became more pronounced following the arrival of Hurricane Katrina in 2005 (see Figure 7). Spot prices skyrocketed following the arrival of Rita.

Sabine Pipeline LLC's Henry Hub, located in south central Louisiana, is the largest centralized point for natural gas spot and futures trading in the United States. There was no trading at Henry Hub for three weeks in 2005 due to a *force majeure* related to lack of power and damaged pipelines at the Hub. As a result, there are disconnects in the 2005 price curves shown on Figure 7. After the Henry Hub resumed operations and trading restarted, spot prices began to fall.

On August 31, 2008, the day before Gustav made landfall, Sabine Pipeline again declared a *force majeure* due to the mandatory evacuation of Vermilion Parish, which included all receipt and delivery points on the Sabine system and the Henry Hub operations. The shut down of the Hub is the cause of the disconnects in the 2008 price curves in Figure 7. In the weeks following the arrival of Hurricanes Gustav and Ike, there was very little movement in the spot price of natural gas, which finished out the year at levels well below 2005.

Working gas is the volume of natural gas stored in an underground reservoir that can be withdrawn (beyond the base or cushion gas that remains permanently in the reservoir). A network of depleted fields, salt caverns, and aquifers is controlled by 112 operators in the United States.[24] Storage maintains reliability of gas supplies during periods of high demand, supports load balancing for pipelines; and it provides arbitrage opportunities for owners of natural gas in storage. Natural gas consumption has a strong seasonal pattern due to its use as a heating fuel. As a result, natural gas is generally injected into storage during the nonheating season (April-October) and withdrawn from storage during the heating season (November-March). This pattern is evident in Figure 8 for the Eastern Consuming Region.[25]

In August 2005, working gas was at its lowest levels in five years. Even though gas demand was low throughout the 2005 hurricane season, working gas storage was unable to recover. By contrast, working gas storage was high in August 2008, and remained healthy throughout the hurricane season. This may have helped dampen price volatility in 2008.

Other factors contributing to a limited price response in 2008 include:[26]

- The 2008 hurricanes were not as powerful as the 2005 storms in terms of wind and storm surge
- Gas processors suffered more extensive damage in 2005 than in 2008, as is evident in the magnitude and duration of the outages
- Interrupted electricity, gas, and petroleum kept a lid on industrial demand for natural gas

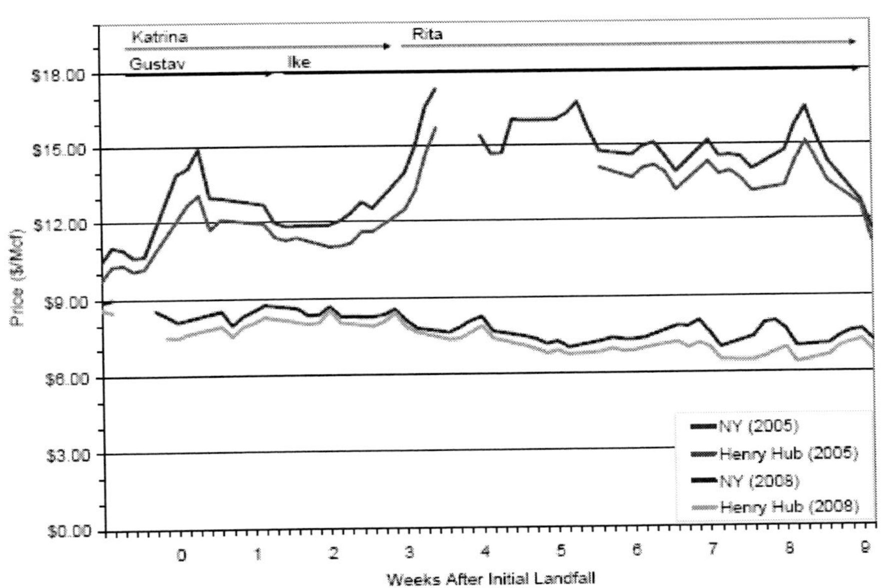

Source: Energy Information Administration, NGI Daily.

Figure 7. Natural Gas Spot Prices during 2005 and 2008 Hurricanes.

PETROLEUM

Production

Hurricanes Gustav and Ike in 2008, and Hurricanes Rita and Katrina in 2005 wreaked tremendous damage on Gulf oil production, refining, and transportation infrastructure, but the damage sustained in 2005 was greater than the damage sustained in 2008.

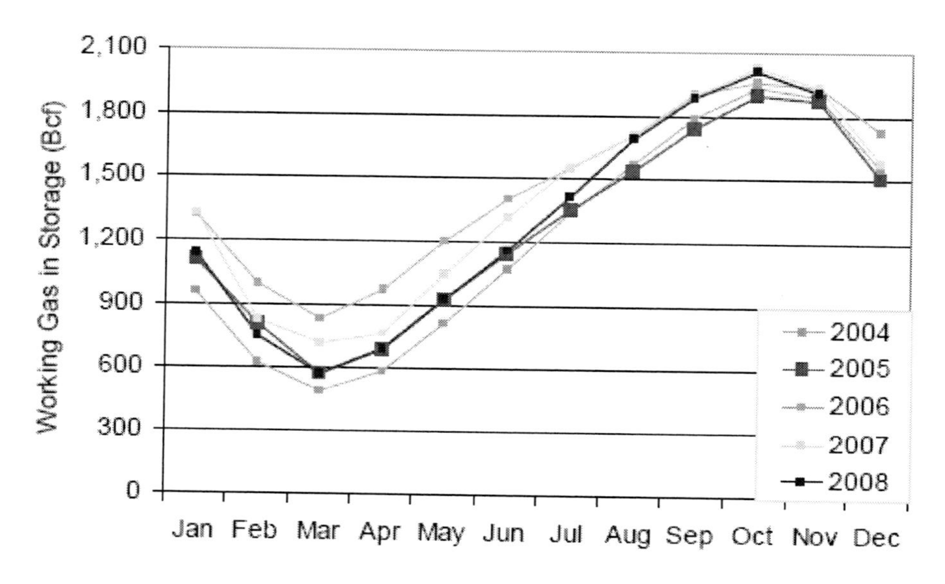

Sources: http://tonto.eia.doe.gov/dnav/ng/hist/n5020882m.htm and http://tonto.eia.doe.gov/dnav/ng/hist/n5020872m.htm.

Notes: Eastern Consuming Regions includes all States east of the Mississippi River less Mississippi and Alabama, plus Iowa, Nebraska and Missouri.

Figure 8. Working Gas in Eastern Consuming Region in 2005 and 2008.

Prior to Hurricane Katrina in 2005, oil production in the federally-administered waters of the Gulf of Mexico stood at 1.5 million barrels/day (MMBD). Hurricane Katrina raced across Florida on August 25, before entering the Gulf of Mexico and causing the shut-in of OCS crude oil production due to evacuations of key personnel and other storm precautions. Katrina caused severe damage to many offshore oil facilities in the Gulf and although some undamaged platforms were quickly brought back online after the storm passed, about 0.8 MMBD, or more than 50 percent of total Gulf production, remained shut-in one month later as Hurricane Rita approached. Again, Gulf platforms were evacuated and 100 percent of oil production was shuttered in advance of Rita.

Initial recovery from Hurricane Rita was tentative and nearly all production remained offline for about one week after the storm passed as companies completed flyovers and damage assessments. After one week, some production was brought back online, but restoration proceeded slowly; seven weeks after Hurricane Rita made landfall, 0.8 MMBD, or about 52 percent, of 2005 Gulf production remained shut in (see Figure 9 and Appendix Table A-5). The pace of restoration was delayed by damaged platforms and gathering pipelines, limited repair equipment and rigs, and the long duration of the 2005 hurricane season. In addition to MMS-monitored Gulf production, Hurricanes Katrina and Rita also forced the shut-in of 0.20 MMBD of oil production in the offshore region three miles off the Louisiana coast, which is monitored by the Louisiana Department of Natural Resources. Nearly one quarter of this production was permanently lost.

Gulf of Mexico crude oil production suffered significant long-lasting damage from the 2005 hurricanes. Before each storm, 80 percent of the Gulf's 819 platforms were evacuated and shut-in. Likewise, almost 70 percent of the Gulf's 134 operating rigs were shut-in before both hurricanes.[27] After the devastation of 2005, a number of platforms were sunk and significant crude oil production capacity was permanently lost, because restoration efforts for certain platforms were too costly.

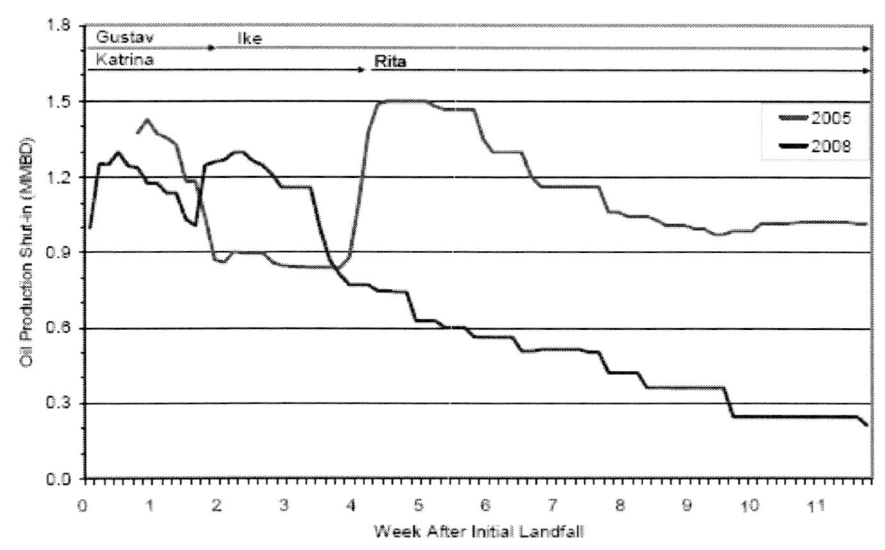

Note: MMS data collection began August 29, 2005, days after Katrina made landfall in Florida, moving across the Gulf. Source: MMS.

Figure 9. Gulf of Mexico OCS Oil Production Shut In by 2005 and 2008 Hurricanes.

One such example was the Typhoon platform operated jointly by Chevron and BHP Billiton 165 miles south of New Orleans. Hurricane Rita severed the moorings to the platform, which capsized during the storm, and was found floating upside-down 80 miles from its original location. The $250-million platform was donated to the MMS artificial reefing program.[28] Nineteen mobile offshore drilling units broke loose from their moorings and were set adrift; some causing damage to pipelines as anchors dragged along the ocean floor.[29] One drifted as far as the Mobile Bridge in Alabama.

Hurricanes Gustav and Ike caused similar but less severe consequences to oil production infrastructure in the Gulf. Due to the lasting effects from the 2005 hurricanes and the natural decline of existing fields, average Gulf production in 2008 was 1.3 MMBD prior to Gustav, 0.2 MMBD below 2005 levels.

The oil industry evacuated platforms and shut in 100 percent of offshore oil production in the Gulf of Mexico as a precaution in advance of Hurricane Gustav. Some of this production came back online after the storm but most of it remained shut-in as operators decided not to return staff to platforms due to the rapid approach of Hurricane Ike. Those platforms that had resumed production after Gustav were shut down again in advance of Ike, which passed well to the west of where Gustav struck before making landfall near Galveston, Texas.

Restoration proceeded quickly at unscathed facilities after operators completed flyovers and damaged assessments but many heavily damaged platforms were unable to restart; seven weeks after Rita made landfall more than 0.4 MMBD, or almost one-third of Gulf production, remained shut in. By February 11, 2009, 0.1 MMBD or 9 percent of OCS crude production remained shut-in.30 Hurricanes Gustav and Ike also shut down most of the 0.16 MMBD of Louisiana DNR-monitored offshore oil production within three miles of the Louisiana coast. By November 17, 2008, 0.12 MMBD of this production had resumed (see Table 5).[31]

Damage to oil production platforms and pipelines was the primary reason that oil production was slow to return after the hurricanes of 2005 and 2008. MMS reported that 113 platforms were destroyed and 52 were damaged out of the 3,050 platforms exposed to hurricane conditions in Gulf of Mexico in 2005. In 2008, by contrast, only 60 platforms were destroyed but 124 were damaged, out of the 2,217 platforms exposed to hurricane conditions. MMS also identified 457 pipelines damaged in 2005, 101 of which were larger diameter pipelines (10 inches or greater). As of early 2009, pipeline damage from Hurricanes Gustav and Ike was still being assessed (see Table 6).

Table 5. Petroleum Operating Capacity in the Gulf of Mexico, 2005 and 2008

Source	2005 Capacity (MMBD)			2008 Capacity (MMBD)		
	Pre-Season	Season Low	Year-End	Pre-Season	Season Low	Year-End
Federal OCS	1.5	0	1.0	1.3	0	1.16
Louisiana DNR	0.2	0.2	0.16	0.16	0.02	0.12

Source: MMS and Louisiana DNR, as reported in ISER Situation reports in 2005 and 2008.

Note: *Date of restoration to full capacity; not the same as restart date.

Table 6. Gulf of Mexico OCS Infrastructure Impacted by 2005 and 2008 Hurricanes

Impacted Infrastructure	2005	2008
Platforms Exposed to Hurricane Conditions	3,050	2,217
Platforms Destroyed	113	60
Platforms Damage	52	124
Pipelines Damaged	457	N/A

Sources: MMS Press Releases #3486 (May 1, 2006), "MMS Completes Assessment of Destroyed and Damaged Facilities from Hurricanes Gustav and Ike," (November 26, 2008).

Refining

In 2005 and 2008, numerous refineries in the Gulf were shut down due to hurricane-induced flooding, wind damage, and loss of electricity. By August 30, 2005, 11 refineries in Louisiana and Mississippi with a combined capacity of 2.5 MMBD were shut down as a precaution in advance of Hurricane Katrina (see Figure 10 and Appendix Table A-5). Hurricane Rita made landfall further west along the Gulf Coast, resulting in the precautionary shut down of 16 additional refineries in Houston, Galveston, Port Arthur and Lake Charles with a combined refining capacity of 4 MMBD. Due to severe damage and flooding, more than 2 MMBD of this capacity remained offline two weeks after Rita's landfall, and about 1 MMBD remained offline four weeks after landfall. In addition, a number of refineries operated at reduced rates for several weeks following the storms.

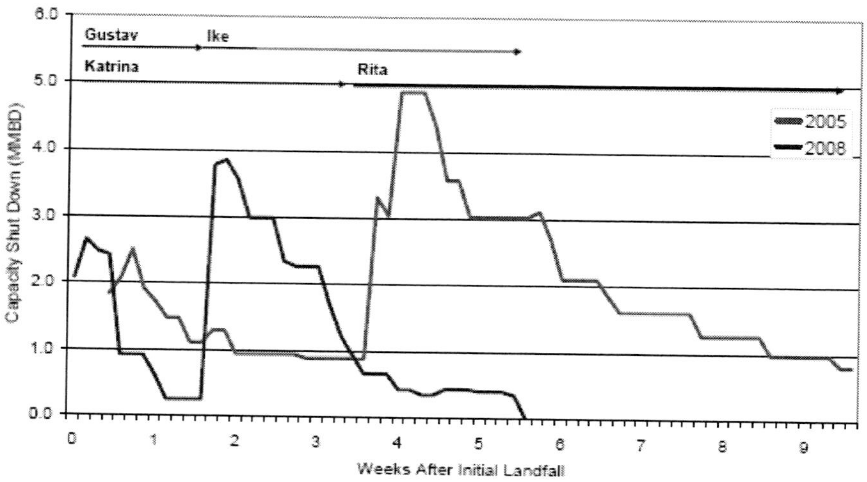

Source: OE/ISER Situation Reports.

Figure 10. Duration of p Refinery Shut Downs during 2005 and 2008 Hurricanes.

In 2008, Hurricanes Gustav and Ike did not hammer Gulf refineries as hard as Hurricanes Katrina and Rita did in 2005. Hurricane Gustav primarily impacted Louisiana refineries, shutting down 14 refineries with 2.7 MMBD of refining capacity along the Lower Mississippi River and in the Lake Charles region. Most of this capacity was shut as a precaution prior to the storm, and 10 days after Gustav all impacted refineries were completely restored to their pre-hurricane capacities. Hurricane Ike, which primarily impacted Texas refineries, shut in nearly 4 MMBD of refining capacity in Houston, Galveston, Port Arthur, and Corpus Christi. Again, much of this capacity was shut as a precaution prior to landfall. Three weeks later, only two refineries remained shutdown, one from complications during restart. Restoration proceeded more rapidly in 2008 because refineries did not experience nearly as much on-site damage. Although some refinery shutdowns lasted from two to three weeks, these outages were primarily caused by lack of electricity supply rather than on-site damage.

Imports & Ports

Hurricanes and tropical storms annually disrupt the imports of crude oil to the U.S. Gulf Coast. September is typically the month with the lowest volume of imports (see Figure 11).[32] Crude oil imports in 2005 were greater than the five-year average in all months except September and October. Crude oil imports to the Gulf fell from 6.4 MMBD in August 2005 to 4.9 MMBD in September 2005 and rose to 5.5 MMBD in October 2005. By contrast, in 2008, crude oil imports to the U.S. Gulf were below the levels of the prior four years in every month. Crude oil imports to the Gulf fell from 6.1 MMBD in August 2008 to 4.4 MMBD in September 2008. This 1.7 MMBD reduction was larger than the drop in 2005.

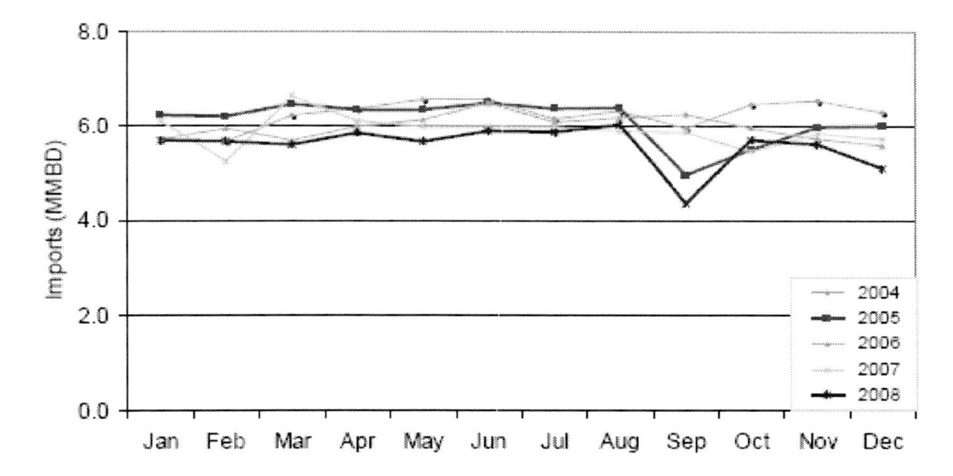

Source: EIA, Imports by Area of Entry, http://tonto.eia.doe.gov/ dnav/pet/hist/ mcrimp31m.htm.

Figure 11. U.S. Gulf Crude Oil Imports, 2005 – 2008.

The U.S Coast Guard announces the closure of major ports and waterways as hurricanes enter the Gulf of Mexico. The Louisiana Offshore Oil Port (LOOP), which receives1 MMBD of crude oil imports, is often shut first. In 2005, the LOOP was shut on August 28, 2005 before Hurricane Katrina made landfall and remained closed until September 3, 2005. Power was not fully restored to the LOOP until September 5, 2005, and imports remained at reduced rates until mid-September, when Port Fourchon became operational. By September 24, 2005, the LOOP was shut again in advance of Hurricane Rita, not to return to full operations until October 3, 2005.

Key waterways were closed starting on August 30, 2005, including the Mobile Ship Channel, Calcasieu Ship Channel, Gulf Intracoastal Waterway from Mobile to New Orleans, and the Mississippi River from the Gulf to Baton Rouge, Louisiana. Within a week, these waterways were back in service, but with draught restrictions and daylight only limitations. These closures and subsequent reduced operations resulted in long queues of crude oil tankers and adversely impacted imports and domestic movements of petroleum products.

When Hurricane Rita entered the Gulf of Mexico, U.S. Coast Guard again announced port closures affecting Houston, Freeport, Port Arthur, and Corpus Christi, Texas. The Port of Houston remained closed September 24 – 26, 2005, and after reopening, operated at reduced levels until September 29, 2005. Port Arthur was closed the longest from September 24-29, 2005, returning to full operations on October 17, 2005.

In 2008, the same ports and waterways were closed in advance of hurricanes Gustav and Ike. The LOOP was closed September 1, 2008 for five days. Tanker offloading resumed on September 5, 2008, only to stop again on September 11 as Ike approached. The LOOP resumed near normal rates on September 16, 2008. The Gulf Intracoastal Waterway was closed on August 31, 2008 from the Louisiana-Mississippi border east to St. Marks, Florida, and reopened on September 5, 2008. A week later, when Hurricane Ike arrived, the Intracoastal was again shut or under restrictions from New Orleans west to Corpus Christi, Texas. The Calcasieu Ship Channel was closed briefly before Gustav and Ike hit, and operated with draft restrictions for weeks. More than 200 miles of the Mississippi River were closed on August 31, 2008. The river reopened with draft restrictions on September 5, 2008. The Army Corps of Engineers closed three Lower Mississippi River locks on September 13, 2008, restricting traffic until September 19, 2008.

In October 2005, gasoline and distillate imports to the Gulf spiked at 6.2 MMB and 2.8 MMB respectively, a ten-fold increase over September 2005 and well beyond volumes seen in any other month.[33] Shutdown refineries with operable ports and connections to the Colonial and Plantation pipelines began importing gasoline and distillate volumes to maintain pipeline flow into the East Coast. State governments sought waivers to import gasoline meeting less stringent quality requirements.[34] Gasoline and distillate imports to the U.S. Gulf retreated back to average levels by November 2005.

The U.S. East Coast also compensated for the lack of pipeline movements from the Gulf by increasing petroleum product imports in 2005. Gasoline imports to the East Coast increased by 3.3 MMB to exceed 18.0 MMB in September 2005 and 20.1 MMB in October 2005. East Coast gasoline imports remained higher than normal through February 2006. The situation was the same for East Coast imports of distillate in 2005. Distillate imports spiked to 11.6 MMB in October 2005 and remained high through February 2006.[35]

A sizeable portion of the additional gasoline and distillate imports in 2005 were due to the delivery of European product reserves from the International Energy Agency. The U.S. government did not request product reserves in 2008.

Gasoline imports to the U.S. Gulf in 2008 also spiked in September and October, but only to 2.5 MMB and 2.0 MMB, respectively.[36] U.S. Gulf distillate imports were almost nonexistent in September-October 2008, as foreign distillate fuel oil did not meet ultra low-sulfur standards required in the United States. East Coast gasoline and distillate imports remained flat from August 2008. Quality restrictions and the timing of the hurricane landfalls in early September 2008 limited the ability of imports to dampen market gyrations.

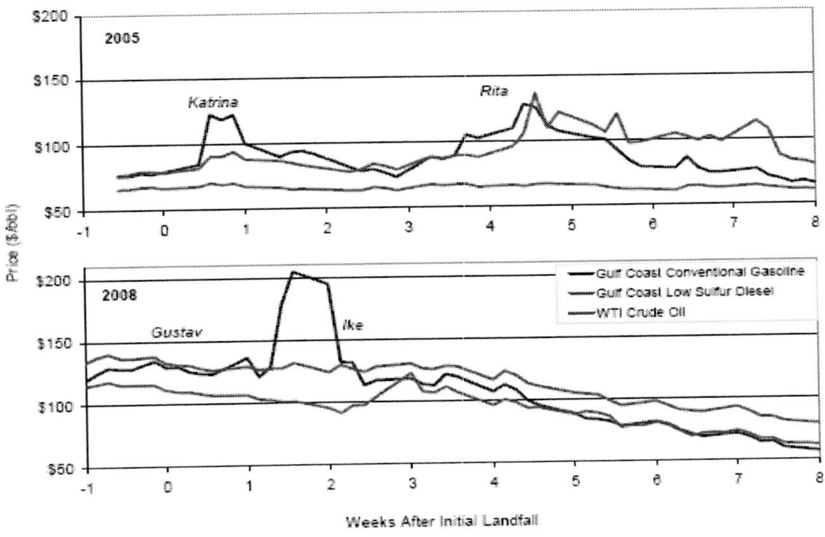

Source: EIA Weekly Prices.

Figure 12. Selected Petroleum Spot Prices during 2005 and 2008 Hurricanes.

Prices and Stocks

Petroleum product prices reacted differently during the 2005 and 2008 hurricane seasons. In 2005, supply disruptions caused by outages at refineries, pipelines and ports, led to sharp spikes in petroleum product prices (see Figure 12). One week prior to Katrina, the price of West Texas Intermediate (WTI) stood at $65 per barrel, the spot price of wholesale gasoline in the Gulf was $75 per barrel, and the spot diesel price in Gulf was $76 per barrel. Although the price of WTI crude oil did not increase significantly during Katrina and Rita, wholesale U.S. Gulf gasoline prices spiked to nearly $125 per barrel (almost $3 per gallon) after Katrina and more than $125 per barrel after Rita. Wholesale U.S. Gulf diesel prices, which increased only slightly after Katrina, surged passed gasoline prices in the week after Rita, spiking to more than $135 per barrel (more than $3.20 per gallon)

The price environment for crude oil and petroleum products in 2008 was vastly different from that of 2005. In 2008 the price of WTI crude oil was about $115 per barrel in the week prior to Gustav's landfall, almost double the price prior to Katrina's landfall in 2005. While crude oil prices were relatively stable in the summer and fall of 2005, oil prices in late summer and fall 2008 were quickly falling from record highs amid an increasingly pessimistic outlook for global economic growth and the weakening U.S. dollar. WTI prices continued to decline during and after Hurricane Gustav and Ike, falling to as low as $91 in the trading week after Ike made landfall in Texas. On September 22, 2008, nine days after Ike's landfall, WTI spiked to close at more than $122, but this price surge may have been attributed to financial investors who had been betting on falling oil prices rushing to cover their positions before the expiry of the October oil futures contract on NYMEX rather than to any production disruptions caused by Hurricanes Gustav and Ike.[37]

Gasoline

U.S Gulf gasoline prices experienced a short-lived spike in 2008. One week before Gustav, the wholesale U.S. Gulf gasoline spot price was about $120 per barrel (about $2.85 per gallon). The spot price rose steadily to $130 per barrel as Gustav approached but decreased after damage to Louisiana refineries proved to not be extensive. In the next week, as Ike approached major refining centers in Houston and Galveston, Texas, traders began to worry about potentially severe damage to refineries and pipelines in the region. In the days before Ike made landfall, U.S. Gulf spot gasoline price spiked sharply, reaching a peak of $204 per barrel (about $4.85 per gallon) on September 12, 2008, the day before Ike made landfall. This was an increase of about 70 percent over the price one week prior to Gustav. After Ike passed, prices remained high for two days as refiners completed assessments and began bringing units back online but then quickly returned to pre-hurricane levels.

The State of Florida used to have a month-long holiday from gasoline taxes. In August 2005, drivers topped off their tanks in advance of Hurricane Katrina's arrival and depleted gasoline stocks. Gasoline stock drawdowns were also experienced by the Gulf States in September and October 2005 as a result of refinery, pipeline and port disruptions caused by Hurricanes Katrina and Rita (see Figure 13). In the week after Hurricane Katrina made landfall, the week ending September 2, 2005, U.S. Gulf gasoline stocks fell by more than 1.7 million barrels to 32.6 MMB and stocks continued to decline for five weeks until mid-October as refinery disruptions from Hurricane Rita exacerbated the drawdown. Despite the initial drawdown after Katrina, wholesale gasoline prices on the Gulf Coast remained cheaper or about the same as the price of gasoline in New York Harbor. As Hurricane Rita approached in late September, however, the Gulf Coast gasoline price began to rise relative to the New York Harbor Price and in the week after Rita made landfall, Gulf Coast prices spiked to 60 cents more than the New York Harbor price. The premium on Gulf Coast gasoline did not disappear until the end of October 2005, after three weeks of large stock builds.

Stock draw downs were similar in 2008. After Gustav made landfall, gasoline production decreased in the Gulf Coast and the Colonial and Plantation pipelines, which serve the Southeast, had to run at reduced capacities and limit volumes on their spur lines. The 2008 hurricane season started with gasoline stocks at 31.2 MMB, 10 percent below 2005 stocks. The disruptions caused by Gustav resulted in a drawdown of 1.8 MMB.

The effect of stock drawdowns on the Gulf gasoline market is apparent in the differentials that developed between gasoline prices in the Gulf and New York Harbor. U.S. Gulf wholesale gasoline was trading 2 cents below New York Harbor gasoline two weeks before Gustav hit. On August 29, 2008, two days before Gustav made landfall, a small premium of about 7 cents had developed in anticipation of the storm. In the week after Gustav, Gulf Coast gasoline prices shot up to a premium of more than 70 cent over the New York Harbor price. As Gulf gasoline stocks increased in late September and early October 2008, Gulf gasoline prices dropped below New York Harbor prices.

Diesel

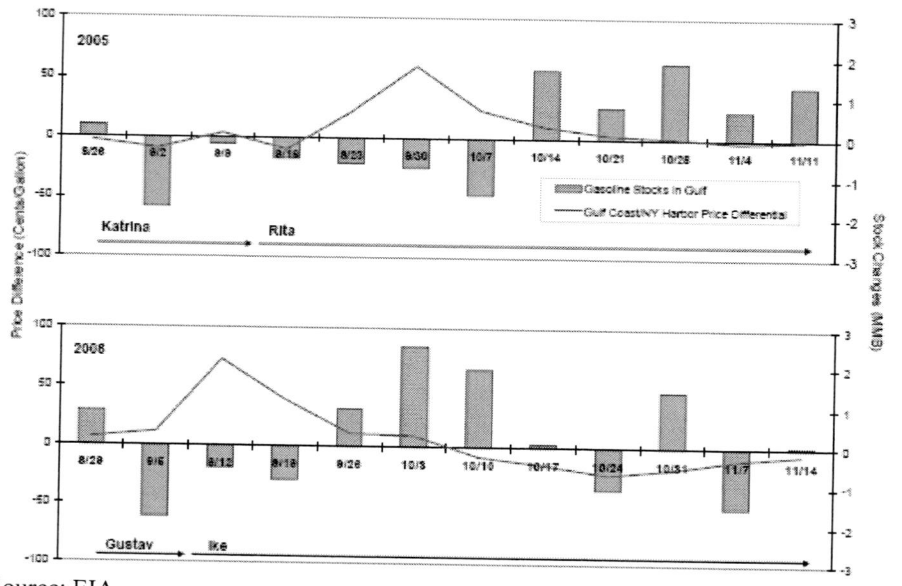

Source: EIA.

Figure 13. U.S. Gulf Gasoline Stocks and Spot Prices during 2005 and 2008 Hurricanes.

In the week before Hurricane Katrina made landfall, diesel stocks in the Gulf Coast stood at just under 23 MMB. The 2005 hurricanes caused significant problems for the distribution of diesel fuel as far away as the Northeast, parts of which rely on supplies of diesel heating oil. U.S. Gulf diesel stocks rose by 2.4 MMB the week after Hurricane Katrina and Gulf wholesale diesel prices continued at parity with New York Harbor prices after the storm passed (see Figure 14). After Hurricane Rita, on the other hand, diesel stocks dropped by about 4.4 MMB, causing the U.S. Gulf spot diesel premium to spike to 48 cents or about 22 percent above the New York Harbor price.

In 2008, movements in diesel stocks and prices were much tamer. In 2006, the U.S. completed a switch from low-sulfur diesel to ultra low-sulfur diesel (ULSD). In the week before Hurricane Gustav made landfall in 2008, Gulf Coast ULSD stocks stood at 24.4 MMB, about 1.4 MMB higher than where low-sulfur diesel stocks stood before Katrina in 2005. Despite a small drawdown in stocks after Gustav, ULSD prices in the Gulf and New York

Harbor remained at parity immediately following the storm. Prior to the arrival of Ike, the Gulf ULSD price saw a 3 percent increase relative to the New York Harbor price, as traders anticipated refinery disruptions. The run up was not nearly as high as the spike seen in gasoline markets. In the week after Ike passed, the U.S. Gulf diesel premium reached as high as 12 cents or about 4 percent above the New York Harbor price. This is one fourth of the spike in diesel prices that occurred in 2005.

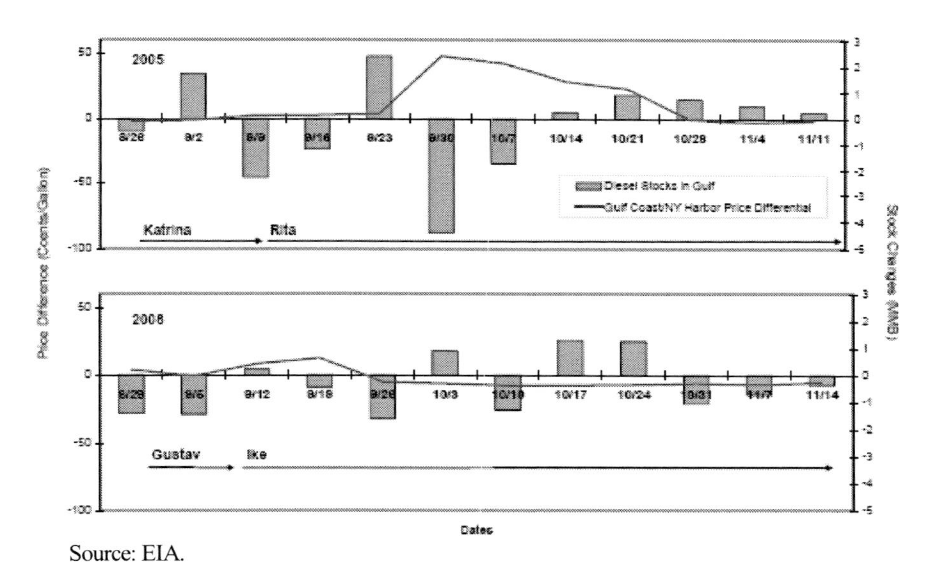

Source: EIA.

Figure 14. U.S. Gulf Diesel Stocks and Spot Prices during 2005 and 2008 Hurricanes.

Transportation and Supply

Most of the crude oil and petroleum products moved through pipelines originate in the Gulf Coast. Production platforms, refineries, ports, and waterways are shut when hurricanes strike the Gulf, and inevitably impact the ability of petroleum pipelines to continue operating. In both 2005 and 2008, pipelines moving crude oil, petroleum products, and liquid petroleum gases were shut entirely, shut partially, or operated at reduced rates for weeks.

Hurricane Katrina's shut down and damage to the LOOP in 2005 resulted in the shut down of the Locap and Capline moving crude oil to refineries. These lines were shut for almost a week and operated at reduced rates for another week until electricity could be restored. While the operators deployed generators, they were unable to maintain normal flows on the pipelines with generators. Electricity loss to pump stations in Louisiana and Mississippi was the cause for the shut down of the Colonial, Dixie, and Plantation pipelines. Reduced refinery output kept the flow of products low on the Colonial and Plantation for a few more days.

Hurricane Rita made landfall further west in Texas, resulting in fewer pipeline shut downs. The Locap, Seaway, Longhorn, and Dixie pipelines shut down as a precaution but were quickly restarted. Almost all of the major product pipelines originating in the Gulf were operating at reduced rates from September 24, 2005 through early October. Reduced refinery output and electricity restoration delayed the return to normal operation.

Only a few major pipelines were shut down by Hurricane Gustav in 2008. The Capline and Locap shut down on September 1, 2008, returning to reduced service four days later. Centennial pipeline was shut on September 2, 2008 and remained down through Ike's landfall, restarting on September 21. Explorer pipeline was shut for one day as a precaution. Colonial, Plantation, and NuStar product pipelines reduced their flows on September 2, and continued in reduced operation through mid-September. Hurricane Ike's arrival resulted in the shut down of Seaway crude, Explorer, NuStar, and Enterprise LPG pipelines. Seaway was impacted by the closure of Freeport terminal. Lack of power at the LOOP kept flow rates low on the Locap and Capline pipelines for a week beginning on September 11, 2008. Reduced refinery operations limited product supply to pipelines for the last two weeks of September 2008. Almost all pipelines returned to normal operations by October 1, 2008.

Similar to 2005, supply shortages developed in some parts of the Southeast in 2008 due to transportation problems – waterborne, pipeline, and highway. Hurricanes Gustav and Ike prevented waterborne petroleum product deliveries from reaching many ports in southeast states and distributors began to truck supplies from nearby states. In some states, marketers with branded supply contracts were put on allocation and independent marketers experienced supply disruptions at stations and terminals.[38] Major oil companies prioritized gasoline supply delivery and generator installation at retail stations along evacuation routes. For example, Florida enacted a new law in 2007 requiring all owners of more than ten gas stations to maintain a generator than can be relocated to stations without power. Owners of more stations are required to have more generators on hand, e.g., 16 locations would require two generators, etc. All portable generators must be stored within the state or within 250 miles of the station, and must be available and in use within 24 hours after the disaster.[39]

As a result, many fueling stations in storm affected areas were able to continue operating on temporary generators until electric power was restored. Supply and power problems at fueling stations were compounded by a surge in demand caused by panic buying as motorists rushed to top off their tanks fearing a repeat of the supply shortages that occurred in some areas following Katrina.[40] Long lines and spot outages of gasoline continued through October 1, 2008 at retail stations in the Georgia, Tennessee, North and South Carolina, and Alabama. According to AAA, Atlanta, Georgia and Charlotte, North Carolina were the cities most affected by the fuel shortages.

Federal & State Actions

The Federal government and State governments coordinated their response to the energy emergencies in 2005 and 2008. Many Federal agencies were involved in the energy sector, including the Department of Energy (DOE), the Department of Homeland Security (DHS), the Department of Transportation (DOT), the Environmental Protection Agency (EPA), the Minerals Management Services (MMS) of the U.S Department of the Interior, U.S. Army Corps of Engineers (ACE), Federal Emergency Management Agency (FEMA), and the Federal Energy Regulatory Commission (FERC). Actions taken by these agencies are summarized below.

Monitoring Infrastructure

DOE is the lead agency for Emergency Support Function #12 (ESF-12), which is intended to facilitate the restoration of damaged energy systems and components when activated by the DHS Secretary for incidents requiring a coordinated Federal response. ESF-12 is an integral part of the larger DOE responsibility of maintaining continuous and reliable energy supplies for the United States through preventive measures and restoration and recovery actions.

ESF-12 collects, evaluates, and shares information on energy system damages and estimates on the impact of energy system outages within affected areas. Additionally, ESF-12 responders provide information concerning the energy restoration process such as projected schedules, percent restored, and geographic progression of restoration.

To achieve these objectives, DOE prepares Emergency Situation Reports, at times twice a day, to provide an official review of the status of energy infrastructure impacted by hurricanes and other natural events deemed to be of national significance. The Situation Reports are distributed widely and posted on the public web site (http://www.oe.netl.doe.gov/emergency_sit_rpt.aspx). In 2005, 93 Situation Reports were prepared; in 2008, 48 Situation Reports were prepared. DOE monitors developments in energy assurance when no emergencies are declared. The Energy Assurance Daily is a newsletter that summarizes the day's major developments and is posted on the public web site as well (http://www.oe.netl.doe.gov/ead.aspx).

Facilitating Restoration

DOE provides 24/7 coverage of the ESF-12 desk at regional FEMA headquarters when they are activated during an emergency. DOE has staff dedicated to serve as regional coordinators and has developed an extensive training program to prepare others to step in during emergencies. Staff are deployed at the National Response Coordination Center (NRCC) in Washington, DC, Regional Response Coordination Centers (RRCC) in each of the ten FEMA regions, state emergency operations centers, joint field offices, and other emergency facilities (see Figure 15).

ESF-12 facilitates the restoration of energy systems through legal authorities. ESF-12 engineers provide technical expertise to the utilities, conduct field assessments, and assist government and private-sector stakeholders to overcome challenges in restoring the energy system.

In response to Hurricane Katrina in 2005, staff began their deployment on August 27, 2005, and most ended by October 9, 2005 except for a joint field office that stayed operational through December 28, 2005. Staff were called up for Hurricane Rita as early as September 18, 2005 and at least one office did not stand down until November 21, 2005. When Hurricane Wilma appeared imminent, staff were again deployed from October 18 through November 29, 2005.

In 2008, ESF-12 deployments were more concentrated in terms of timing, but not geography. In 2008, FEMA Regions II & III (Mid-Atlantic), IV (Southeast), V (MidContinent) and VI (Gulf Coast) all requested ESF-12 support in their regions during a three week time period due to Gustav and Ike. ESF-12 staff remained in Texas months after Ike to assist with the electricity recovery efforts, especially related to temporary housing.

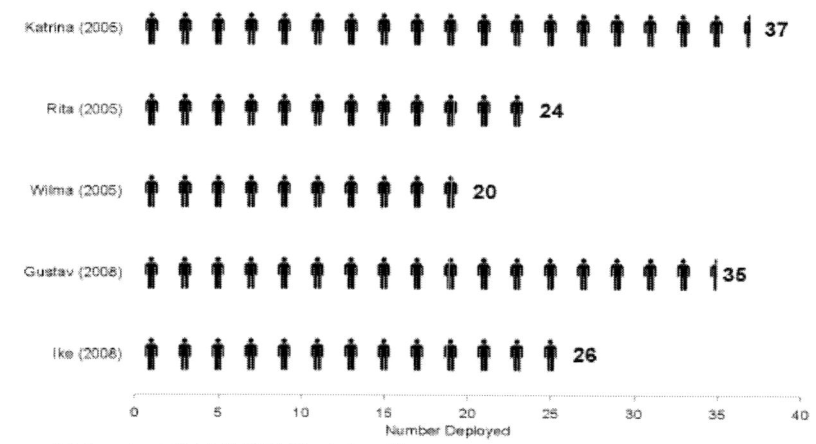

Source: Volpentest HAMMER Training Center.

Figure 15. ESF-12 Deployments during Major Hurricanes in 2005 and 2008.

Prioritizing Power Restoration

DOE has the authority to invoke Section 202(c) of the Federal Power Act, which gives the Secretary of Energy the authority to determine that an "emergency" exists, and "to require by order such temporary connection of facilities and such generation, delivery, interchange, or transmission of electric energy as in [the Secretary's] judgment will best meet the emergency and serve the public interest." Section 202(c) was invoked both in 2005 and 2008 to provide an emergency interconnect to the Livingston Pumping Station which supplies Houston with water. CenterPoint provided the emergency connection to the facility normally supplied by Entergy. DOE issued a second 202(c) order in 2005 to authorize and direct TXU Electric Delivery to temporarily connect and energize its existing Huntington to Etoile 138kV line for the purpose of delivering electricity to Deep East Texas Electric Cooperative, an area normally served by Entergy Gulf States, Inc. DOE also worked with pipeline, terminal, and power companies to coordinate restoration efforts by establishing Collins Tank Farm in Mississippi as a priority for power restoration. This tank farm is a significant location for Colonial and Plantation pipelines. Generators were brought instead and DOE worked with DOT to institute driver and weight limit waivers and to ensure that generators were delivered.

DOE also assisted an electricity pole producer in Alabama by facilitating delivery of distillate fuel on a priority basis to continue manufacturing poles needed for electricity recovery in the Gulf Coast region in 2005.

Strategic Petroleum Reserves

The Department of Energy's Strategic Petroleum Reserve (SPR) was fundamental in the Department's response to the 2005 and 2008 hurricanes. The SPR mission is to diminish the vulnerability of the United States to the harmful effects of petroleum supply disruptions, to meet U.S. obligations under the international energy program, and to maintain the ability to respond to an emergency. By virtue of their locations in Louisiana and Texas, SPR sites were impacted during both hurricane seasons. On August 28, 2005, SPR shut down operations in New Orleans, West Hackberry and Bayou Choctaw, Louisiana, primarily due to flooding.[41] Shutdowns continued until the water receded and electricity was restored. SPR facilities at Bryan Mound and Big Hill, Texas were fully operational throughout Hurricane Katrina. West Hackberry and Big Hill were without power due to Hurricane Rita for about a week. Nonetheless, DOE activated the SPR when the facilities were restored, and invited companies to bid competitively on purchases and loans of available crude.

In 2005, nine Gulf Coast and Midwest refiners requested more than 24 MMB of crude oil from SPR (see Figure 16), equal to more than 16 days of full Gulf of Mexico oil production. Requests were made between August 29 and September 4, 2005. Deliveries of crude to refiners were completed by October 25, 2005. Over 13 MMB came in the form of exchanges in which the refiners were required to repay loans with physical barrels at a later date; all crude oil was returned to SPR by June 30, 2007. The remaining 11 MMB were disbursed through competitive auctions.

Three SPR sites were closed by the 2008 hurricanes: Bryan Mound, Texas: Big Hill, Texas; and West Hackberry, Louisiana; were impacted by storm surge and accessible only by boat for a week. In 2008, only 5.4 MMB were requested by five refiners who were impacted by Mississippi River and ship channel closures. All of these deliveries were made in the form of exchanges. Marathon and Placid were the only refiners to request oil in both 2005 and 2008.

In addition to domestic supplies of crude oil, the DOE can seek emergency release of petroleum product reserves in Europe. On September 2,

2005, the United States obtained 60 MMB of petroleum product stocks from the International Energy Agency (IEA), the first such release since the first Iraq war in 1991.[42] IEA member countries hold about 4.1 billion barrels of public and industry oil stocks, of which, roughly 1.4 billion barrels are government controlled for emergency purposes. Unlike the SPR, which contains crude oil, the IEA reserves are all petroleum products. In September 2008, the United States coordinated with TEA but no formal request was made.

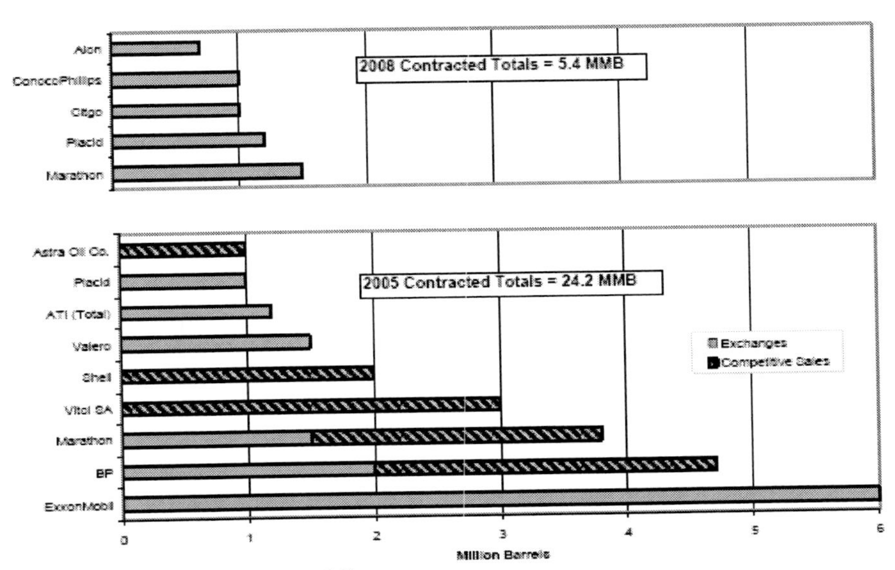

Source: DOE Fossil Energy Techlines.

Figure 16. Refiner Requests for U.S. Strategic Petroleum Reserves 2005 and 2008.

Waivers

FERC Power Transaction Waivers

On September 4, 2008, the Federal Energy Regulatory Commission (FERC) granted Entergy two emergency waivers that allowed the company to manage their resources in the wake of Hurricane Gustav. FERC granted the company a waiver of the one-month minimum term for unit power sales and resales between the Entergy operating companies.

FERC also allowed Entergy's operating companies to enter into transactions that include capacity from the Grand Gulf nuclear power plant without advance FERC approval. These waivers were in effect only where an Entergy operating company experienced a significant loss of load as a result of the hurricane, and only until the emergency conditions from the hurricane subsided.

Jones Act Waivers

DOE worked with DHS to provide due diligence, i.e., DOE collaborated with other Federal agencies to assess whether an energy emergency existed that would necessitate a temporary waiver. Following Hurricane Katrina, DHS waived the Merchant Marine Act of 1920 (the "Jones Act") for certain shipments of crude oil and petroleum products in the Gulf. The Jones Act prohibits foreign built, owned, or flagged vessels from carrying goods between U.S. ports. The waiver, which was effective from September 1 to 19, 2005, allowed large foreign flagged tankers to assist U.S. vessels in the transportation of crude oil and refined products from the Gulf Coast to other parts of the country to alleviate supply problems caused by the shutdown of Gulf refineries and pipelines.[43] On September 26, 2005, after the passage of Hurricane Rita, DHS issued another Jones Act Waiver, effective until October 24, 2005. No Jones Act waivers were requested during the 2008 hurricane season.

EPA Fuel Waivers

Following the hurricanes of 2005 and 2008, EPA waived certain fuel requirements in order to facilitate supply logistics and increase import flexibility. DOE worked closely with EPA to provide due diligence to facilitate decision-making regarding temporary waiver of certain fuel requirements. In 2005, EPA granted widespread fuel waivers to states impacted by supply disruptions caused by Hurricanes Katrina and Rita (see Figure 17). Thirty states and the District of Columbia, stretching from the east to west coasts and as far north as New England, requested and were granted waivers for gasoline, diesel fuel, or both by the EPA. Seven states - the five Gulf Coast states plus Georgia and Virginia – received fuel waivers for both gasoline and diesel. In addition, EPA issued a waiver for the entire United States covering the two weeks after Katrina's landfall of the requirement to sell summer gasoline and allowing the early use of higher volatility wintertime gasoline. Within the same waiver, the EPA also allowed the use of on-highway diesel fuel that exceeds 500 ppm sulfur content.

In 2008, by contrast, fuel waivers were limited primarily to the Gulf Coast and southeastern United States and were granted only for gasoline (with the exception of Texas which received waivers for both gasoline and diesel).

Drive Hour Waivers

DOE worked with the DOT Federal Motor Carrier Safety Administration (FMCSA) to approve a driver-hour waiver for motor carriers hauling emergency relief supplies, including emergency fuel supplies, in the Southern and Eastern regions of the country.[44] The waiver was issued on September 14, 2005 and expired on October 5, 2005. The waiver was extended nationwide through October 26, 2005. In addition, the governors of many states experiencing fuel shortages due to disruptions caused by Hurricanes Katrina and Rita declared states of emergency, triggering temporary suspension of certain Federal safety regulations, including driver hours for tanker trucks carrying fuel. On September 13, 2008, FMCSA issued a regional emergency declaration affecting six Southern states – Alabama, Georgia, Louisiana, Mississippi, North Carolina, and South Carolina. The declaration and driver hour waiver for truckers delivering fuel-related supplies was extended through October 15, 2008.[45]

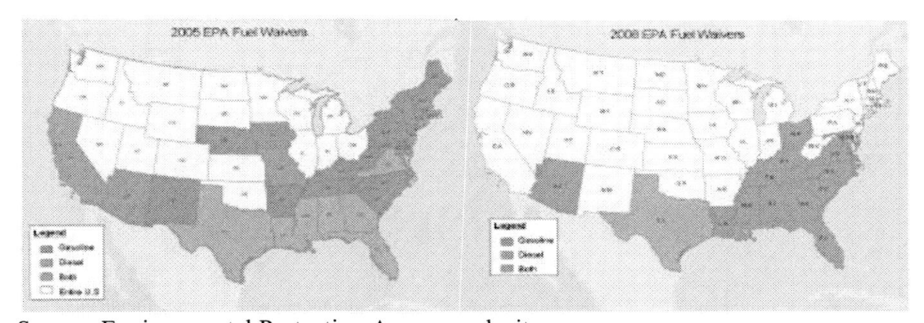

Source: Environmental Protection Agency web site.

Figure 17. Fuel Waivers Issued by EPA to States in 2005 and 2008.

Price Gouging

DOE monitors fuel prices to make certain that consumers pay appropriate prices at the pump. During emergencies, DOE opens its price gouging hotline (1-800-224-3301) and web site (www.gaswatch.energy.gov) for consumers.

EIA monitors regional inventories and prices weekly, sharing data with the Federal Trade Commission and state energy offices.

At least 29 states plus the District of Columbia have laws that prohibit price gouging at fuel stations after a natural disaster, although the definition of “price gouging” varies from state to state. Maine and Michigan have declared price gouging illegal at all times within their states. Arkansas considers price gouging illegal following any disaster while Georgia and Texas tie these laws to a natural disaster or emergency declaration.

It is difficult to account for all the emergency declarations in 2005. The governors of at least five States– Alabama, Florida Louisiana, Mississippi, and Texas – declared State Emergencies, followed by FEMA declarations of federal disasters. In addition, the President declared emergencies in 45 states and the District of Columbia in order to approve federal aid for evacuees from Hurricane Katrina.[46]

In 2008, eight states declared emergencies due to Hurricane Gustav and 11 states declared emergencies due to Hurricane Ike (see Figure 18). Five Gulf Coast states – Florida, Alabama, Mississippi, Louisiana, and Texas – declared states of emergency for both storms.

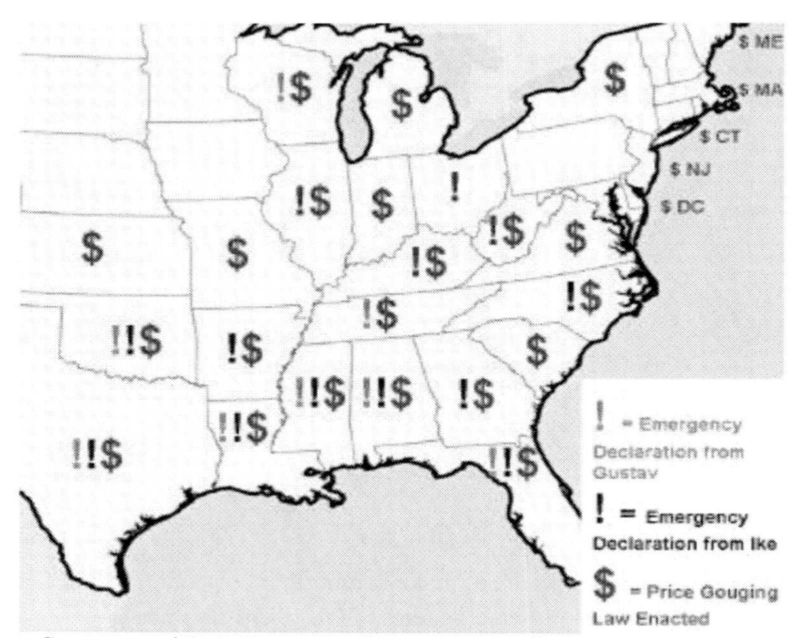

Source: Governor and State Emergency Management web sites.

Figure 18. 2008 Emergency Declarations and Anti-Gouging Laws by State.

APPENDIX TABLES

Table A-1. 2005 Hurricane Electricity Impacts

Million Customers by State	Pre-Katrina 1/1/2005	Worst Day Outages		Outages 2 Weeks Later	Hurricane Wilma 10/25/05	Outages 6 Weeks Later
		Katrina 8/30/05	Rita 9/25/05	10/11/05		11/7/05
Alabama	2.4		0.8	-		
Arkansas	1.5	-	-	-		
Florida	9.2		0.2	-	3.5	0.1
Louisiana	2.2	0.8	0.7	0.1		
Mississippi	1.4	0.9	-	-		
Texas	10.4	-	0.8	<0.05		
Total	27.0	2.7	1.5	0.2	3.5	0.1

Sources: OE/ISER Situation Reports.

Table A-2. 2008 Hurricane Electricity Impacts

Million Customers by State	Pre-Gustav 1/1/08	Worst Day Outages		Outages 2 Weeks Later	Outages 4 Weeks Later	Outages 6 Weeks Later
		Gustav 9/2/08	Ike 9/14/08	9/29/08	10/14/08	10/28/08
Arkansas	1.5	-	0.2	-	-	-
Louisiana	2.1	1.1	0.2	-	-	-
Mississippi	1.4	0.1	-	-	-	-
Texas	10.7	-	2.5	0.2	<0.1	<0.1
Other States*	27.5	-	1.0	-	-	-
Total	43.3	1.1	3.9	0.2	<0.1	<0.1

Source: OE/ISER Situation Reports.

* The storm quickly moved north impacting Missouri, Kentucky, Indiana, Illinois, Ohio, and New York through 9/15/08.

Table A-3. 2005 Hurricane Natural Gas Impacts

Natural Gas Production, Processing & Pipelines	Pre-Katrina Production	Worst Day Outages		Outages 2 Weeks Later	Outages 4 Weeks Later	Outages 6 Weeks Later
		Katrina	Rita			
	8/24/2005	8/30/2005	9/25/2005	10/11/2005	10/25/2005	11/7/2005
Natural Gas Production Billion Cubic Feet per Day	10	8.8	8.1	6.0	5.6	4.5
	100%	88%	81%	60%	56%	45%
% of Gulf	19%	17%	15%	11%	11%	9%

Table A-3. (Continued)

Natural Gas Production, Processing & Pipelines	Pre-Katrina Production	Worst Day Outages		Outages 2 Weeks Later	Outages 4 Weeks Later	Outages 6 Weeks Later
		Katrina	Rita			
	8/24/2005	8/30/2005	9/25/2005	10/11/2005	10/25/2005	11/7/2005
Production % of U.S. Production						
Processing Gulf processors (number) Billion Cubic Feet per Day % of Gulf Capacity % of U.S. Capacity	NA 25.7 100% 33%	NA NA NA NA	NA 17.1 67% 22%	NA 9.5 37% 12%	NA 8.1 32% 11%	NA 7.9 31% 10%
Interstate Longhaul Pipelines Pipelines Shutdown Pipelines Reduced	None None					

Sources: MMS and EIA.

Table A-4. 2008 Hurricane Natural Gas Impacts

Natural Gas Production, Processing & Pipelines	Pre-Gustav Production	Worst Day Outages		Outages 2 Weeks Later	Outages 4 Weeks Later	Outages 6 Weeks Later
		Gustav	Ike			
	8/28/2008	9/2/2008	9/14/2008	9/29/2008	10/14/2008	10/28/2008
Natural Gas Production Billion Cubic Feet per Day	7.4	7.1	7.3	3.9	2.7	2.5
% of Gulf Production	100%	95%	98%	53%	37%	33%
% of U.S. Production	14%	13%	14%	7%	5%	5%
Processing						
Gulf processors (number)	97	25	30	6	5	5
Billion Cubic Feet per Day	25.7	16.1	14.5	3.4	3.2	3.2
% of Gulf Capacity	100%	63%	57%	13%	12%	12%
% of U.S. Capacity	33%	21%	19%	4%	4%	4%
Interstate Longhaul Pipelines Pipelines Shutdown	None	None	None	None	None	None
		ANR; Columbia Gulf;	ANR; Columbia Gulf;			
		Gulf South; NGPL	Gulf South; NGPL			
		America;	America;	ANR;		

Natural Gas Production, Processing & Pipelines	Pre-Gustav Production	Worst Day Outages		Outages 2 Weeks Later	Outages 4 Weeks Later	Outages 6 Weeks Later
		Gustav	Ike			
	8/28/2008	9/2/2008	9/14/2008	9/29/2008	10/14/2008	10/28/2008
		Northern	Northern	Columbia Gulf;		
		NG; Southern NG;	NG; Southern NG;	Southern NG; Texas		
Pipelines Reduced	None	Tennessee Gas;	Tennessee Gas;	Eastern; Texas Gas;	None	None
		Texas Eastern; Texas	Texas Eastern; Texas	Transcontine ntal;		
		Gas;	Gas;	Trunkline		
		Transcontine ntal;	Transcontine ntal;			
		Trunkline	Trunkline			

Sources: MMS, EIA, OE/ISER Situation Reports.

Table A-5. 2005 Hurricane Petroleum Impacts

Petroleum Production, Refining & Pipelines	Pre-Katrina Production	Worst Day Outages		Outages 2 Weeks Later	Outages 4 Weeks Later	Outages 6 Weeks Later
		Katrina	Rita			
	8/24/2005	8/30/2005	9/25/2005	9/29/2008	10/14/2008	10/28/2008
Crude Oil Production Million Barrels per Day % of Gulf Production % of U.S. Production	1.5 100% 30%	1.4 93% 28%	1.5 100% 30%	1.1 71% 21%	1.0 69% 20%	0.8 52% 15%
Refining Gulf refineries (number) Million Barrels per Day % of Gulf Capacity % of U.S. Capacity	34 7.3 100% 42%	11 2.5 34% 14%	20 4.9 67% 28%	7 1.9 25% 11%	4 1.0 14% 6%	3 0.8 11% 5%
Petroleum Pipelines Crude Pipelines Shutdown Crude Pipelines Reduced Product Pipelines Shutdown Product Pipelines Reduced	None None None None	LOOP; Capline None Colonial; Plantation; Dixie None	LOOP; Sun; Seaway;TEPPCO Capline Explorer; TEPPCO; Longhorn; Dixie Colonial	None Capline; Sun None Explorer; TEPPCO	None None None None	None None None None

Sources: MMS and OE/ISER Situation Reports.

Table A-6. 2008 Hurricane Petroleum Impacts

Petroleum Production, Refining & Pipelines	Pre-Gustav Productio n	Worst Day Outages		Outages 2 Weeks Later	Outages 4 Weeks Later	Outages 6 Weeks Later
		Gustav	Ike			
	8/28/2008	9/2/2008	9/14/2008	9/29/2008	10/14/2008	10/28/2008
Crude Oil Production Million Barrels per Day % of Gulf Production % of U.S. Production	1.3 100% 26%	1.3 100% 26%	1.3 100% 26%	0.7 57% 15%	0.5 39% 10%	0.4 28% 7%
Refining Gulf refineries (number) Million Barrels per Day % of Gulf Capacity % of U.S. Capacity	33 7.5 100% 43%	14 2.7 35% 15%	15 3.9 51% 22%	2 0.4 6% 2%	0 0.0 0% 0%	0 0.0 0% 0%
Petroleum Pipelines Crude Pipelines Shutdown Crude Pipelines Reduced Product Pipelines Shutdown Product Pipelines Reduced	None None None None	LOOP; Capline; Marathon; Sunoco Centennial Colonial; Plantation	Marathon; Sunoco; Genesis LOOP; Capline Centennial; NuStar; Explorer; Longhorn; Seaway; Enterprise Colonial; Plantation; Magellan;TEP PCO; Dixie	Marathon; Genesis None None Centennial; CP; Explorer; Longhorn; Magellan; Plantation	None None None None	None None None None

Sources: MMS, AOPL, and OE/ISER Situation Reports.

End Notes

[1] Between July 23 and September 13, 2008, Hurricanes Dolly, Gustav, and Ike; and Tropical Storms Edouard and Hanna made landfall in the United States. Hurricane Dolly made landfall on the Texas-Mexico border and had only minor impacts to U.S. energy infrastructure.

[2] http://apps.shareholder.com/sec/viewerContent.aspx?companyid=ETR&docid=3925483 and http://investor.shareholder.com/entergy/secfiling.cfm?filingID=65984-05-323.

[3] http://www.entergy.com/news room/newsrelease.aspx?NR ID=981.

[4] The peak outages from the storm, as monitored and reported in OE/ISER Energy Assurance Daily were closer to 7 million, but the timing did not coincide with the release of the Hurricane Ike Situation Reports.

[5] http://www.novec.com/documents/CoopLivingOct05.pdf

[6] http://www.reuters.com/article/domesticNews/idUSN0350182220080903.

[7] http://www.nei.org/keyissues/safetyandsecurity/factsheets/nuclearplantsstructural strengthkatrinapage2/

[8] MMS Press Release #3418, January 19, 2006, http://www.mms.gov/ooc/press/2006/ press0119.htm.

[9] Louisiana In-State Production Weekly Status Update, 1/5/09, http://dnr.louisiana.gov/sec/execdiv/pubinfo/weeklyonshore-prod.ssi. The parishes included in DNR survey are Acadia, Assumption, Calcasieu, Cameron, Iberia, Jefferson, Jefferson Davis, Lafayette, Lafourche, Orleans, Plaquemines, St. Bernard, St. Charles, St. Martin, St. Mary, Terrebonne, and Vermilion.

[10] http://tonto.eia.doe.gov/oog/special/eia1_katrina.html.

[11] MMS Press Release #3486, May 1, 2006, http://www.mms.gov/ooc/press/2006/press0501.htm.

[12] U.S. Department of Energy, "Impact of the 2005 Hurricanes on the Natural Gas Industry in the Gulf of Mexico Region," July 31, 2006, http://www.fossil.energy.gov/programs/oilgas/publications/naturalgas_general/hurricane_report05.pdf.

[13] MMS Press Release #3933, November 26, 2008, http://www.mms.gov/ooc/press/2008/press1126a.htm

[14] *Ibid* and MMS Press Release #3958, February 11, 2009, http://www.mms.gov/ooc/press/2009/press0211.htm.

[15] Louisiana DNR has not issued any updates since November 17, 2008.

[16] MMS Press Release #3902, October 7, 2008, http://www.mms.gov/ooc/press/2008/press1007c.htm and Bruce Nichols, "Post-Ike gas line fixes slow return of US Gulf oil," Reuters, December 11, 2008.

[17] U.S. Department of Energy, "Impact of the 2005 Hurricanes on the Natural Gas Industry in the Gulf of Mexico Region," July 31, 2006,http://www. fossil.energy.gov/programs/oilgas/publications/naturalgas general/hurricane report05.pdf.

[18] EIA, Impact of the 2008 Hurricanes on the Natural Gas Industry, http://www.eia.doe.gov/pub/oil_gas/natural_gas/feature_articles/2009/nghurricanes08/nghurricanes08.pdf.

[19] EIA-757, Schedule B, Natural Gas Processing Plant Survey, http://www.eia.doe.gov/pub/oil_gas/natural_gas/survey_forms/eia757bf.pdf.

[20] EIA, Impact of the 2008 Hurricanes on the Natural Gas Industry, http://www.eia.doe.gov/pub/oil_gas/natural_gas/feature_articles/2009/nghurricanes08/nghurricanes08.pdf.

[21] According to corporate press releases, three gas processors were due to come on line in December 2008 and the final two processors were to return to service by the end of second quarter 2009.

[22] Black Marlin Pipeline, Chandeleur Pipeline, Dauphin Island Gathering, Destin Pipeline, Discovery Gas Transmission, Enbridge (UTOS), Garden Banks Gas Pipeline, High Island Offshore System, Manta Ray Offshore gathering, Mississippi Canyon Pipeline, Nautilus Pipeline, Sea Robin Pipeline, Stingray Pipeline, and Venice Gathering System are the 14 gathering lines.

[23] ANR Pipeline, Columbia Gulf Transmission, Gulf South Pipeline, Kinder Morgan Tejas Interstate, Kinder Morgan Texas Interstate, Natural Gas Pipeline Co. of America, Northern Natural Gas Pipeline, Sabine Pipeline (Henry Hub), Southern Natural Gas, Tennessee Gas Pipeline, Texas Eastern Transmission, Texas Gas Transmission, Transcontinental Gas Pipeline, and Trunkline Gas Pipeline are the 14 interstate pipelines.

[24] EIA, U.S. Storage Drawdown Analysis Report, March 2008, http://www.eia.doe.gov/pub/oil_gas/natural_gas/feature_articles/2008/ngstordrawdown/ngstordrawdown.pdf.

[25] Eastern Consuming Regions includes all States east of the Mississippi River less Mississippi and Alabama, plus Iowa, Nebraska and Missouri.

[26] EIA, Impact of the 2008 Hurricanes on the Natural Gas Industry, http://www.eia.doe.gov/pub/oil_gas/natural_gas/feature_articles/2009/nghurricanes08/nghurricanes08.pdf.

[27] MMS Press Release #3418, January 19, 2006, http://www.mms.gov/ooc/press/2006/ press 0119.htm.

[28] "Chevron to Sink Typhoon Platform Damaged by Hurricane," May 9, 2006, http://www.bloomberg.com/apps/news?pid=10000081&sid=a0J.TXumCtVQ&refer=australia.

[29] Atkins, et.al., Pipeline Damage Assessment from Hurricanes Katrina and Rita in the Gulf of Mexico, prepared by Det Norske Veritas AS for MMS, Rpt # 448 14183, March 15, 2007.

[30] MMS Press Release #3958, February 11, 2009, http://www.mms.gov/ooc/press/2009/press0211.htm.

[31] Louisiana In-State Production Weekly Status Update, January 5, 2009, http://dnr.louisiana.gov/sec/execdiv/pubinfo/weekly-onshore-prod.ssi. Louisiana DNR has not updated these values since November 17, 2008.

[32] EIA, Imports by Area of Entry, http://tonto.eia.doe.gov/dnav/pet/hist/mcrimp31m.htm.

[33] *Ibid.*

[34] Reid Vapor Pressure (RVP) and sulfur requirements during summer driving season.

[35] *Ibid.*

[36] *Ibid.*

[37] Javier Blas and Chris Flood, "Oil price jumps $25 in a day," Financial Times, 9/22/08, http://www.ft.com/cms/s/0/a42969f2-88e1-11dd-a179-0000779fd18c.html.

[38] Keith Reid, "Gustav and Ike Rattle Southeastern Supply," NPN web, 10/24/08,http://www.npnweb.com/ME2/dirmod.asp?sid=3B7062773CE64BBC9CC064EED2542B6B&nm=Industry+Issues &type=MultiPublishing&mod=PublishingTitles&mid=8F3 A7027421841978F18BE895F87F791&tier=4&id=748D CA5017FE4DAD97B6C96CBB65383Al.

39 http://www.fpma.org/upload library/082106Generatorbill.pdf.

40 *Ibid.*

[41] DOE" The Strategic Petroleum Reserve Reaction to Hurricanes Katrina And Rita" presentation at Petrostocks 2007, http://www.petrostock.org/2007/Presentations/ Gibson,%20Hoot/Hoot%20Presentation.pdf.

[42]IEA Press Release, "IEA Announcement of Emergency Stock Release," 9/2/05, http://www.iea.org/Textbase/press/pressdetail.asp?PRESS REL ID=155.

[43] http://npga.org/files/public/Jones Act Waver 9-05.pdf

[44] http://www.fmcsa.dot.gov/about/news/news-releases/2005/hosrelief.htm.

[45] http://www.fmcsa.dot.gov/emergency/SSC-Ruban-fuel-shortage-extension-dec-100708.pdf.

[46] http://www.fema.gov/news/disasters.fema.

In: U.S. Energy Industry Response ...
Editor: Ilya Bertolucci

ISBN: 978-1-62808-944-8

Chapter 3

STATEMENT OF PATRICIA HOFFMAN, ASSISTANT SECRETARY, OFFICE OF ELECTRICITY DELIVERY AND ENERGY RELIABILITY, U.S. DEPARTMENT OF ENERGY. HEARING ON "WEATHER-RELATED ELECTRICAL OUTAGES"*

Chairman Bingaman, Ranking Member Murkowski, thank you for the opportunity to appear before you today to discuss the Department of Energy's (DOE) role in managing weather related electrical outages. DOE plays a vital role, in coordination other Federal agencies and industry to prepare for and recover from such electric power outages. Given the recent increase of severe weather incidents, including the recent tornadoes in Texas and the Midwest, and the approach of the 2012 hurricane season, this discussion is especially timely and important.

DOE'S ROLE, RESPONSIBILITIES AND AUTHORITIES

The mission of the Office of Electricity Delivery and Energy Reliability (OE) is to lead national efforts to modernize the electric grid, enhance the security and reliability of the Nation's energy infrastructure, and facilitate

* This is an edited, reformatted and augmented version of a statement, presented April 26, 2012 before the Senate Committee on Energy and Natural Resources.

recovery from disruptions to the energy supply. As the Sector-specific Agency for Energy, under the Department of Homeland Security's National Infrastructure Protection Plan (NIPP), the DOE's Office of Electricity Delivery and Energy Reliability is responsible for collaborating with Federal, State and local governments, and the private sector to protect against and mitigate threats on the energy infrastructure, be they natural disasters, deliberate attacks, or human error. OE performs the functions required under DOE's authorities and Presidential Policy Directive (PPD) – 8, National Preparedness, which is aimed at strengthening the security and resilience of the United States through systematic preparation for the threats that pose the greatest risk to the security of the Nation, including acts of terrorism, cyber attacks, pandemics, and catastrophic natural disasters. In addition, DOE is the lead agency for the National Response Framework's Emergency Support Function 12 (ESF-12), Energy, when activated by the Federal Emergency Management Agency (FEMA), under the Robert T. Stafford Disaster Relief and Emergency Assistance Act.

In the event of an emergency, OE stands up its Emergency Response Center and has a team of responders that specialize in energy infrastructure who can be quickly activated and deployed to the location of an event. OE personnel then coordinate with deployed personnel, other DOE offices, and Federal, State and local agencies in responding to the emergency. OE provides situational awareness and facilitates the restoration of energy systems. In addition, OE may provide technical expertise to utility companies, conduct field assessments, and assist government and private-sector stakeholders to overcome challenges in restoring the energy system.

REPORTING ON ENERGY EMERGENCY SITUATIONS

Reporting on emergency events plays a crucial role in helping other government agencies and industry prepare for and recover from energy outages resulting from these events. Reporting also allows the public to remain informed of the situation and plan accordingly.

OE takes great care in providing timely, accurate reports and situational assessments. When a major energy outage occurs, there is often a surge of information. Because the situation changes rapidly during these events, there are sometimes conflicting outage reports and incomplete information on damage status. In such cases, we must review and sift through large amounts of data and information to make certain that reported information is relevant, trustworthy, and accurate.

Through years of working closely with our Federal, State, local, and private partners in response to energy emergencies, OE has established proven procedures for evaluating and reporting outage data and situational assessments. OE maintains a team of trained staff at our DOE headquarters and field offices, which are prepared to assist in situational assessment, response, and reporting for any event. Procedures have been established for data collection, quality control, and reporting. These procedures are implemented for sudden events including unexpected severe weather (e.g., tornadoes, earthquakes, floods) as well as events such as hurricanes where we have the opportunity to pre-position staff and develop a timeline for data collection and reporting.

OE personnel use a standardized process for data collection, assessment, quality control, and reporting. The process is documented and repeatable and uses data sources that are fully referenced. As a result, we are able to provide high quality reports quickly and efficiently.

OE obtains data from a number of resources. Data on electrical outages are received through the OE-417 Form, "The Electric Emergency Incident and Disturbance Report," which provides timely information to DOE when utilities experience electrical incidents. We also collect information on damage to the infrastructure directly from energy companies such as utilities whenever possible. Many energy companies, including larger utility companies, now provide real-time outage information on their websites. We also use an in-house software tool which allows us to monitor the Nation's energy infrastructure in near real-time and create geospatial maps of the Nation's energy assets and systems that combine data from numerous sources into a single geographic information system (GIS). This system is known as the Environment for Analysis of Geo-Located Energy Information (EAGLE-I).

We also gather data and information from trained ESF-12 staff that have been deployed to the field, to FEMA, and to other locations during emergency events. These ESF-12 responders provide situational assessments and facilitate clear and consistent communication with other deployed responders. They also help to provide subject matter expertise to aid in restoration activities and identify where the Federal government can engage in restoration efforts if and when appropriate.

OE reviews all of the collected information, determines what information is relevant and appropriate to report, and evaluates the quality of the data source, and the date and time it was generated. If we identify discrepancies, we resolve them by investigating the discrepancy and determining which information is correct and current.

OE provides a situational assessment that includes State-by-State outage totals, the number and percent of customers without power, the scope of the damage within each State, utility restoration efforts, when restoration is expected to occur, whether any critical assets have been damaged, what response measures are being reported by ESF-12 teams, and what is being implemented by the energy companies. This information is then compiled into Situation Reports that are time-stamped and include references to all data sources. The Situation Reports are then made available to the public online (http://www.oe.netl.doe.gov/emergency sit rpt.aspx). The Situation Reports provide a snapshot of a given point in time, and are shared with Federal agencies responsible for making critical emergency response decisions. OE considers these reports as the Federal Government's official report on the scope of the damage and status of restoration at a specific point in time. These situational assessments facilitate decision making surrounding Federal response efforts and provide a much needed national perspective to State and local government as well as the private sector.

We recognize that actual outage numbers can change moment-to-moment during a given weather event. As a storm system moves through an area, the number of customers without power can change rapidly. Following a storm, as utility crews work to restore power, outage numbers will continue to change hour-to-hour as repairs are made. Figure 1 below is an example of customer power outages reported during Hurricane Irene and shows the rate of restoration over a nine-day period. As seen in the Figure, the majority of customers had their power restored within 3 days.

Situation Reports provide a common frame of reference on the severity, scope, and location of the impact. These situation assessments combined with our subject matter experts support decision making on when and if there is an appropriate role for Federal involvement in the restoration process. For example, the Situation Reports are used by FEMA and the U.S. Army Corp of Engineers to help determine where supplies of water, ice, food and generators should be delivered.

Because the energy sector focuses on their specific service territories during outage events, and States and local governments focus on their specific jurisdictions, OE's Situation Reports are a definitive source for obtaining a nationwide perspective on the outage, looking at the entire affected region and energy infrastructure as a system. The Situation Reports are considered a "one-stop" shop for energy infrastructure information.

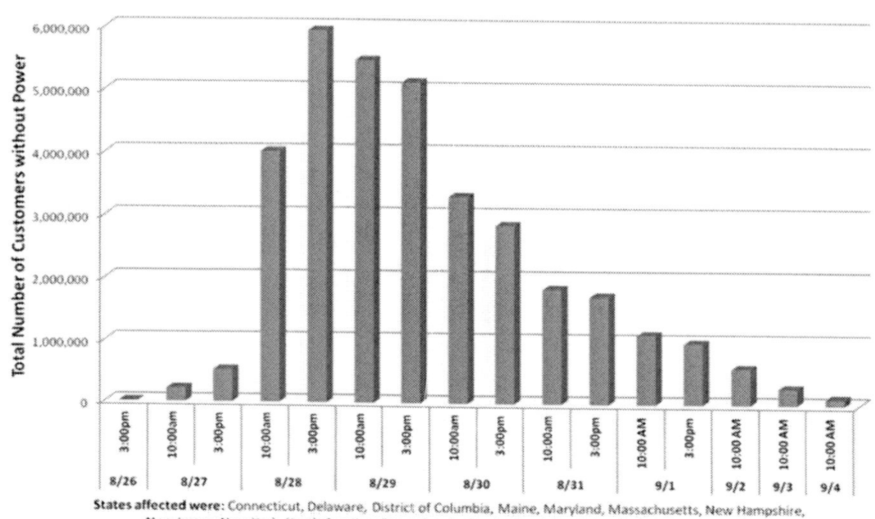

Source: DOE Situation Reports.

Figure 1. Customer Power Outages from Hurricane (2011).

Because OE understands the energy infrastructure, we are often called upon to help evaluate if requests for temporary waivers of certain regulations are warranted. The most frequent types of requests are to temporarily suspend Clean Air Act fuel requirements, use of foreign flagged vessels under the Jones Act, and to allow the interconnection of one utility to another under Section 202(c) and (d) of the Federal Power Act. We work closely with and provide the necessary due diligence to assist Federal agencies with evaluations of the severity and duration of the event and work with them to determine if waiver requests are justified.

DOE staff maintain constant communication with our Federal partners such as the Department of Homeland Security, including FEMA; Department of Transportation; Department of Defense; and the Environmental Protection Agency; State agencies in the affected area; and the energy companies impacted by the event.

OE provides a common frame of reference on the location, scope and potential duration of an event. This common frame of reference is critical for determining appropriate response measures. It enables us to communicate the presence of any critical infrastructure assets so they can be established as a priority in the restoration effort. It also gives those leading the response efforts sound information to determine where the application of Federal resources can facilitate a faster restoration.

ONGOING EFFORTS

DOE is very aware that the private sector owns and operates the vast majority of our Nation's energy assets. OE works closely with the owners and operators of the energy infrastructure, as well as State and local governments. Throughout the year, OE collaborates with these organizations to prepare for energy emergencies resulting from both weather-related and manmade emergencies. OE conducts workshops and tabletop exercises, provides resources and support for energy assurance planning, and facilitates relationship building across these organizations. The communications channels that these activities have fostered have proven to be invaluable when major outages occur.

We regularly evaluate our procedures to identify opportunities for improvement. On an ongoing basis, OE gathers information from public sources such as media outlets and creates a summary of public information about current energy issues. To help stakeholders stay current on energy infrastructure events, OE publishes the Energy Assurance Daily (EAD) to report on developments affecting energy systems, flows, and markets. The EAD is available to the public online (http://www.oe.netl.doe.gov/ead.aspx).

In an effort to continue improving communication and sharing of information, DOE works with industry groups such as the Edison Electric Institute, to emphasize the importance of providing timely, accurate, and consistent data by their members companies that is crucial during recovery and restoration periods. OE encourages industry to use terminology that is understandable to the response community and to the general public. We also stress the importance of company websites in providing continually updated information on those customers without power, locations and restoration times. I would also like to highlight the follow-up that OE has done with private sector companies to ascertain the improvements they have made over the past several years, particularly since the 2005 and 2008 hurricane seasons. An OE report titled "Hardening and Resiliency: U.S. Energy Industry Response to Recent Hurricane Seasons," notes that industry has undertaken numerous actions to harden their energy systems by replacing wooden poles with concrete or steel, strengthening poles with guy wires, elevating substations and control rooms, and improving their vegetation management practices and supply logistics. In addition, companies have taken innovative approaches to deploy sensors such as Phasor Measurement Units to determine the health of their systems. Companies are also making investments by installing composite poles, using infrared thermography to scan and identify problems on their transmission lines, and integrating smart grid technology.

Advanced smart grid technologies can reduce restoration time significantly. For example, the Electric Power Board (EPB) of Chattanooga, a Recovery Act Smart Grid Investment Grant recipient, is installing automated feeder switches, fiber communications, and sensor equipment for distribution circuits that can be used to detect faults and automatically switch to reroute power and restore other customers. In April 2011, severe storms caused power outages for three-fourths of EPB customers – 129,000 residences and businesses. Smart grid technologies installed earlier helped EPB reduce outage time significantly by clearly identifying the location and extent of the damage. EPB was also able to avoid sending repair crews out 250 times. In September of 2011, another storm knocked out power to 59,000 homes and businesses. EPB determined that its smart grid technologies, in that situation, prevented an additional 25,000 customers from losing power.

In April 2011, Alabama suffered significant tornado damage. Southern Company, a Recovery Act Smart Grid Investment Grant recipient that has invested in smart grid technologies that improve outage communication and provide restoration notification during storms, had more than 412,000 customers without power as a result of the severe weather. Between Monday, April 27 and Wednesday, April 29, Alabama Power (a subsidiary of Southern) was able to restore power to over 200,000 of its customers. By the following Monday, May 1, 95 percent of the affected customers had had their power restored. Two days later, on Wednesday, May 3, restoration was nearly complete at 99.9 percent.

CONCLUSION

Reporting accurate, timely, and actionable information during emergencies is critical to helping Federal, State and local government agencies, the private sector, and the general public be more aware of impacts to the energy infrastructure and helping to minimize the impact of hazards.

As we move into the summer months, this year's hurricane season and beyond, we remain vigilant and focused on our vital roles and responsibilities in reporting quickly and accurately on energy outages, working with our partners on response and restoration efforts, and keeping the American public informed. Although we hope the recent forecast for a light 2012 hurricane season is an accurate one, we are prepared for this year's events and whatever they may bring.

This concludes my statement, Mr. Chairman. I look forward to answering any questions that you and your colleagues may have. Thank you.

INDEX

D

G

H

I

O

P

Q

R

O

P

Q

R

S

V

W